keyboard theory

Preparatory Book A

By Grace Vandendool

ISBN 0-88797-477-5

FREDERICK
HARRIS
MUSIC

Foreword

The KEYBOARD THEORY series was written in response to the needs of music students in private and classroom instruction. It attempts to bridge the difficulties students encounter when relating basic music theory to the practical application of learning an instrument.

A visual approach—the relationship between theory and the keyboard—is emphasized throughout the series to simplify the learning of new concepts. All explanations and instructions are kept short, simple and easy to understand. Reviews at the end of each chapter, covering current and previously learned concepts, help students to retain and test their knowledge.

KEYBOARD THEORY is a progressive series of exercise books written to provide the young student with a thorough knowledge of the fundamentals of music theory.

Acknowledgements

I would like to thank the following people for their devoted efforts in the preparation of this publication:

Editor:	Melissa Vandendool
Music Engraving & Typesetting:	Musictype Limited
Cover Art:	Linda Post
Illustrations:	Melissa Vandendool

I would also like to thank my husband and children for their constant encouragement to write this book.

GRACE VANDENDOOL

To my husband

Contents

Lesson No. 1   The Keyboard..   6

Lesson No. 2   The Clefs...   16

Lesson No. 3   Line and Space Notes   20

Lesson No. 4   Notes in the Treble Clef..   26

Lesson No. 5   Notes in the Bass Clef...   54

Lesson No. 6   Time: Note and Rest Values   82

Lesson No. 7   Common Terms and Signs...   94

LESSON No. 1

The Keyboard

The **BLACK KEYS** are arranged in groups of:

TWO'S   and THREE'S

The **WHITE KEYS** have the same letternames as the first **SEVEN LETTERS** of the **ALPHABET: A   B   C   D   E   F   G.**

EXAMPLE:

1. **C** is the white key which is always found to the **LEFT** of the **TWO BLACK KEYS.**

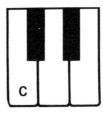

NAME every **C** on this keyboard.

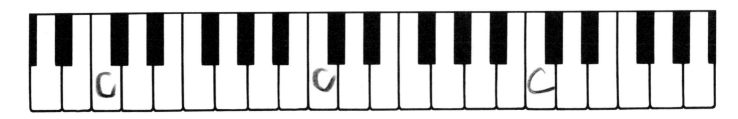

2. **D** is the white key which is always found **BETWEEN** the **TWO BLACK KEYS**.

NAME every **D** on this keyboard.

3. **E** is the white key which is always found to the **RIGHT** of the **TWO BLACK KEYS**.

NAME every **E** on this keyboard.

4. **F** is the white key which is always found to the **LEFT** of the **THREE BLACK KEYS**.

NAME every **F** on this keyboard.

5. **G** is the white key which always **FOLLOWS F.**

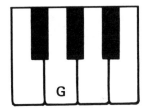

NAME every **G** on this keyboard.

6. **A** is the white key which always **FOLLOWS G.**

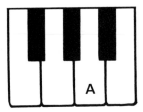

NAME every **A** on this keyboard.

7. **B** is the white key which is always found to the **RIGHT** of the **THREE BLACK KEYS.**

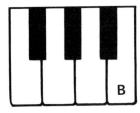

NAME every **B** on this keyboard.

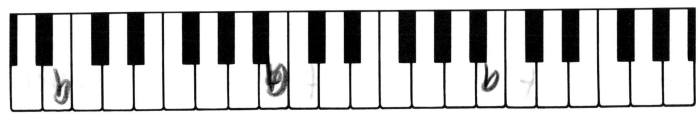

8. **NAME EVERY KEY** on the following keyboards.

a.

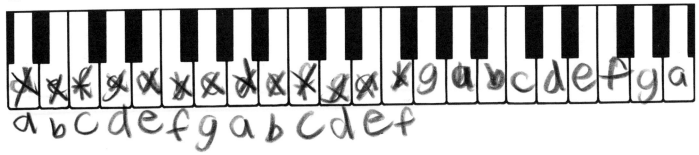

b.

9. Fill in the **MISSING LETTERS** of the musical alphabet.

a.

b.

c.

10. NAME the keys marked with an "X".

EXAMPLE:

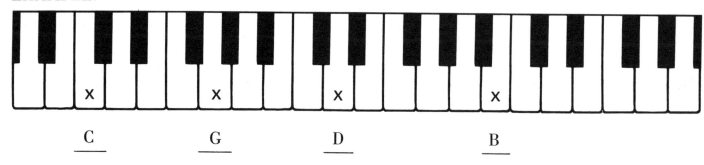

C   G   D   B

a.

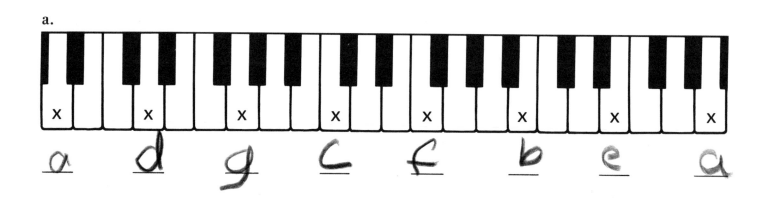

a   d   g   c   f   b   e   a

b.

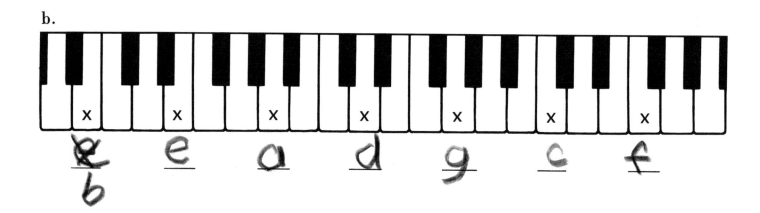

e   e   a   d   g   c   f
b

c.

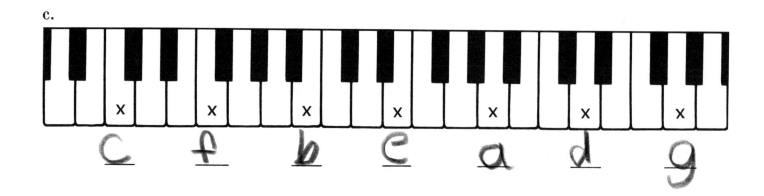

C   f   b   e   a   d   g

11.
The Musical Alphabet Song

G. Vandendool

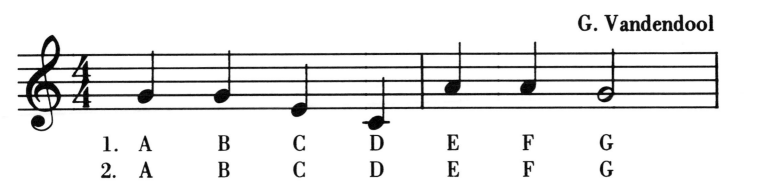

1. A   B   C   D   E   F   G
2. A   B   C   D   E   F   G

is   the   mu - si - cal   al - pha - bet.
A   B   C   D   E   F   G

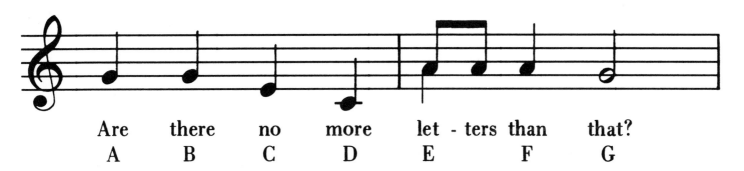

Are   there   no   more   let - ters than   that?
A   B   C   D   E   F   G

Fine

No   no   no   no   no   no   NO!
is   the   mu - si - cal   al - pha - bet.

D.C. al Fine

spoken: What's   the   mu - si - cal   al - pha - bet?

12. **NAME** the keys marked with an "X". They spell words.

EXAMPLE:

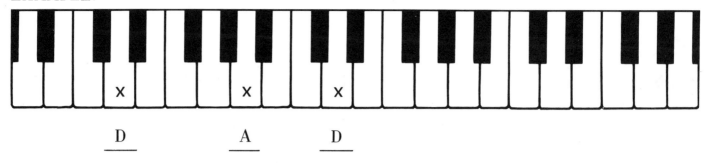

D   A   D

a.

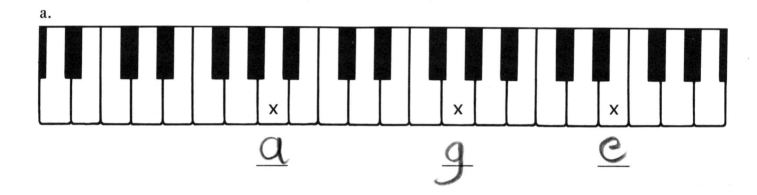

a   g   e

b.

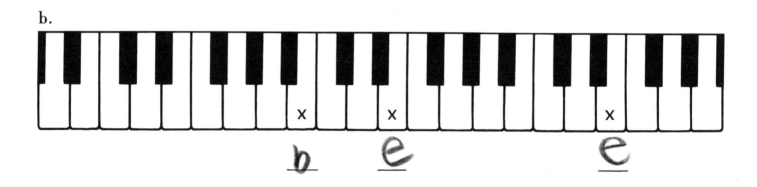

b   e   e

c.

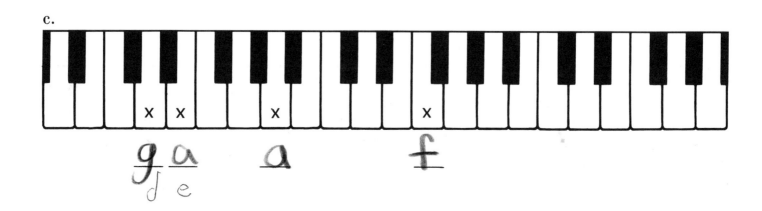

g a   a   f
d e

13. **WRITE** the following **WORDS** on the keyboard.

EXAMPLE: E G G:

a.   **B A D:**

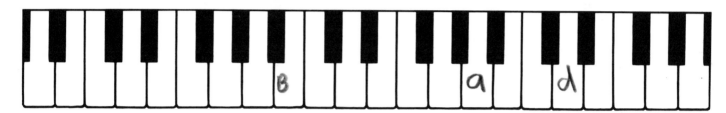

b.   **E D G E:**

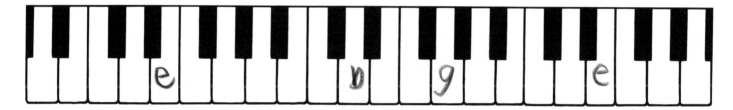

c.   **B A B E:**

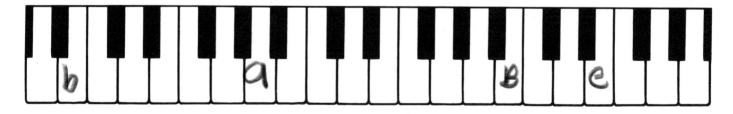

d.   **F E E:**

14.

Keyboard Crossword Puzzle

NAME the keys marked with an **"X"** on the keyboards below and write the **WORDS** they form on the crossword puzzle.

ACROSS

1.
3.
5.
7.
8.
9.
10.

DOWN

1.
2.
4.
6.
9.
11.
12.

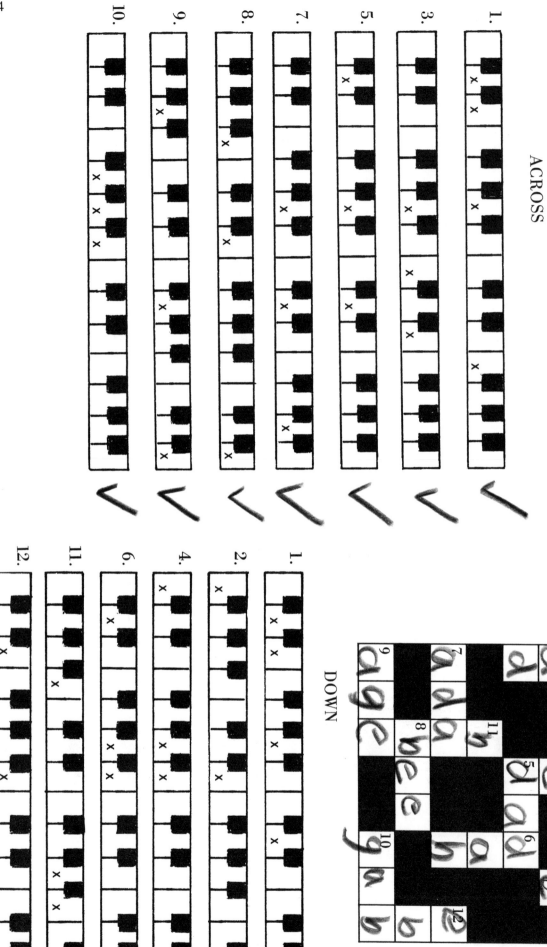

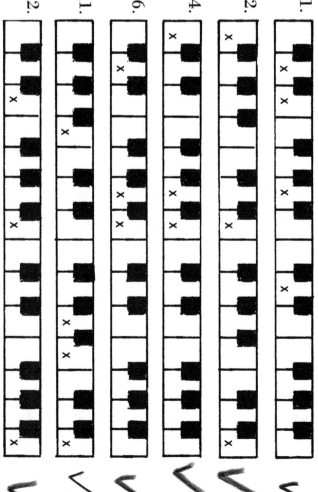

Excellent!

REVIEW No. 1

50

7   1. What are the **LETTERNAMES** of the musical alphabet?

a   b   c   d   e   f   g

20   2. **NAME ALL** the **WHITE KEYS** on the keyboard.

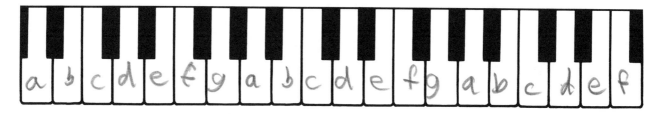

a b c d e f g a b c d e f g a b c d e f

15   3. **NAME** the keys marked with an **"X"**.

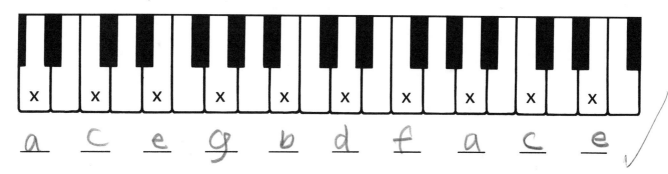

a   c   e   g   b   d   f   a   c   e

4   4. **NAME** the keys marked with an **"X"**. They spell a word.

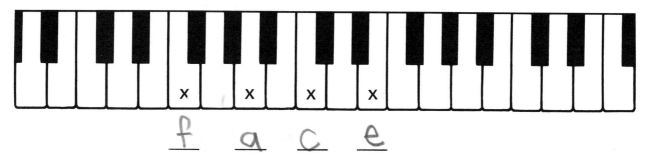

f   a   c   e

4   5. **WRITE** the following **WORD** on the keyboard.

BADE:

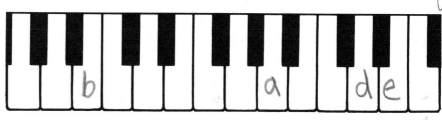

b   a   d e

The Clefs

I am a **TREBLE CLEF.**

I identify the **HIGHER-SOUNDING NOTES** on the keyboard.

I am usually played by the **RIGHT HAND.**

There are 5 steps to draw me:

1. Draw a straight line with a curve at the bottom.

2. Count UP 4 lines and make a dot.

3. Make your first loop.

4. Make your second loop.

5. Make your third loop and stop just below the second line.

EXAMPLE:

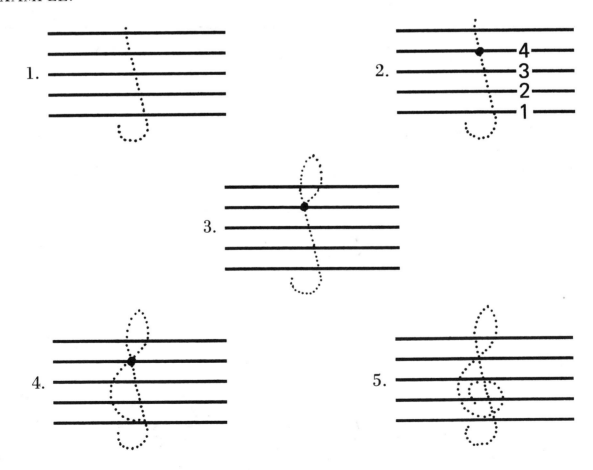

Because I stop just below the G line I am also called a **G CLEF.**

EXERCISES:

1. I am a **TREBLE CLEF** or **G CLEF**. **TRACE** me!

a.

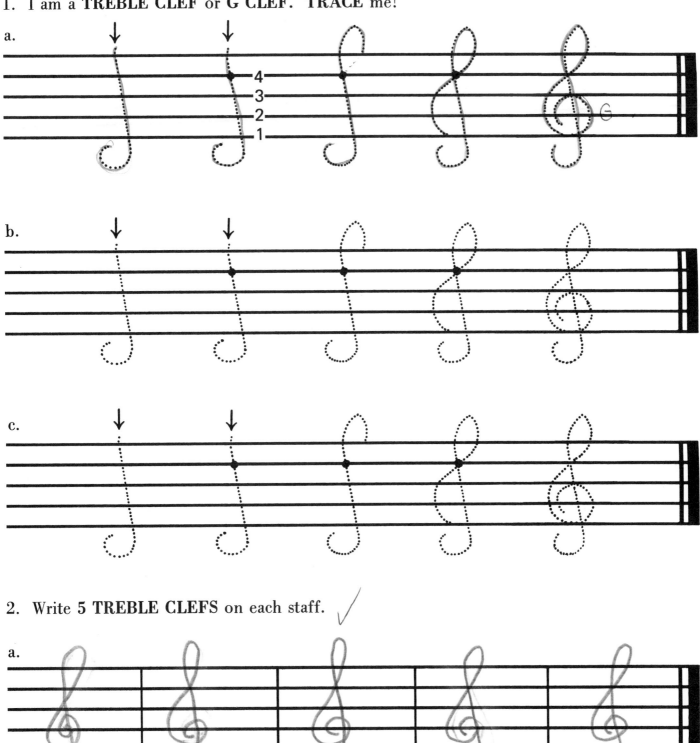

b.

c.

2. Write **5 TREBLE CLEFS** on each staff.

a.

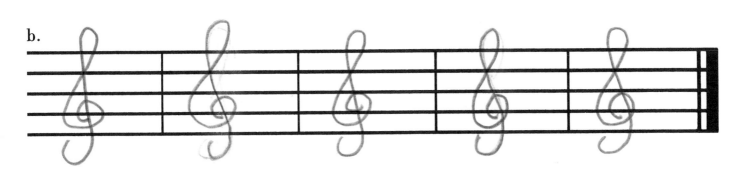

b.

I am a **BASS CLEF.**

I identify the **LOWER-SOUNDING NOTES** on the keyboard.

I am usually played by the **LEFT HAND.**

There are 3 steps to draw me:

1. Draw a dot on line 4.

2. Make a curve, stop just below line 2.

3. Write the dots in spaces 3 and 4.

EXAMPLE:

1.

2.

3.

Because I start on the **F LINE,** I am also called a **F CLEF.**

EXERCISES:

1. I am a **BASS CLEF** or **F CLEF**. **TRACE** me!

a.

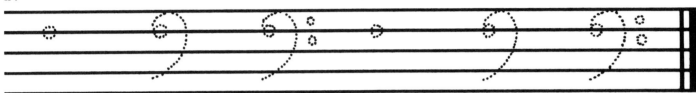

b.

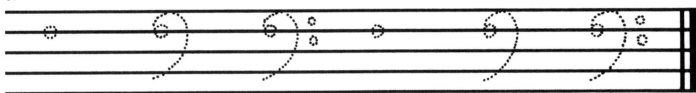

c.

2. Write **5 BASS CLEFS** on each staff.

a.

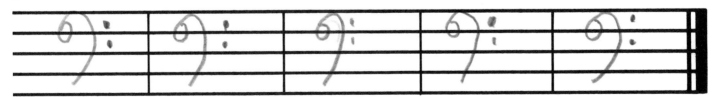

b.

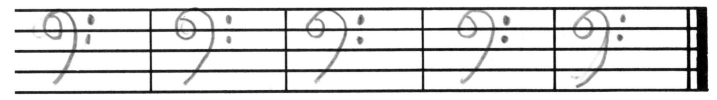

LESSON No. 3

Line and Space Notes

1. Notes are written on lines and in spaces between the lines.
2. The lines and spaces are called the **STAFF**.

3. There are 5 LINES on the staff.

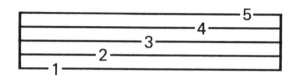

EXERCISES:

NUMBER the **LINES** 1, 2, 3, 4 & 5 on the staffs below.

Notes

a.

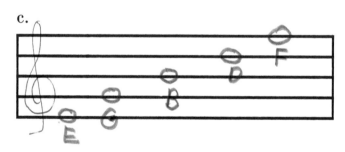

b.

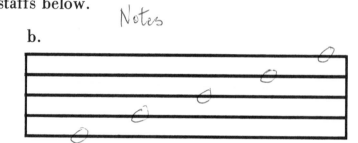

c.

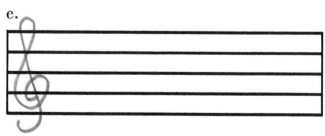

d.

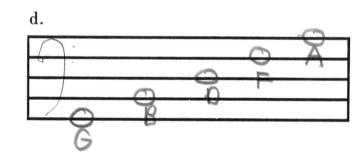

Name the Notes

e.

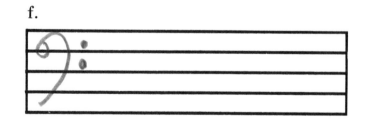

f.

g.

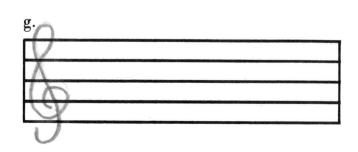

h.

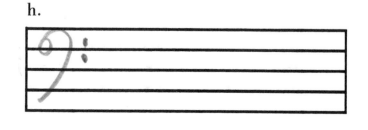

4. There are 4 SPACES on the staff.

EXERCISES:

NUMBER the SPACES 1, 2, 3 & 4 on the staffs below.

a.

b.

Notes

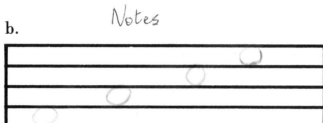

c.

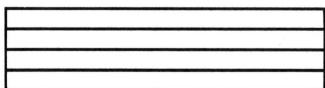

F   A   C   e

Name the notes

d.

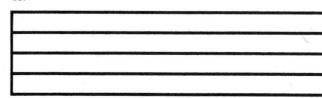

A   C   E   G

Excellent!
QR

e.

f.

g.

h.

5. LINE NOTES are written on the **LINES**:

EXERCISES:

Write a **NOTE** on every **LINE** starting from the **bottom line.**

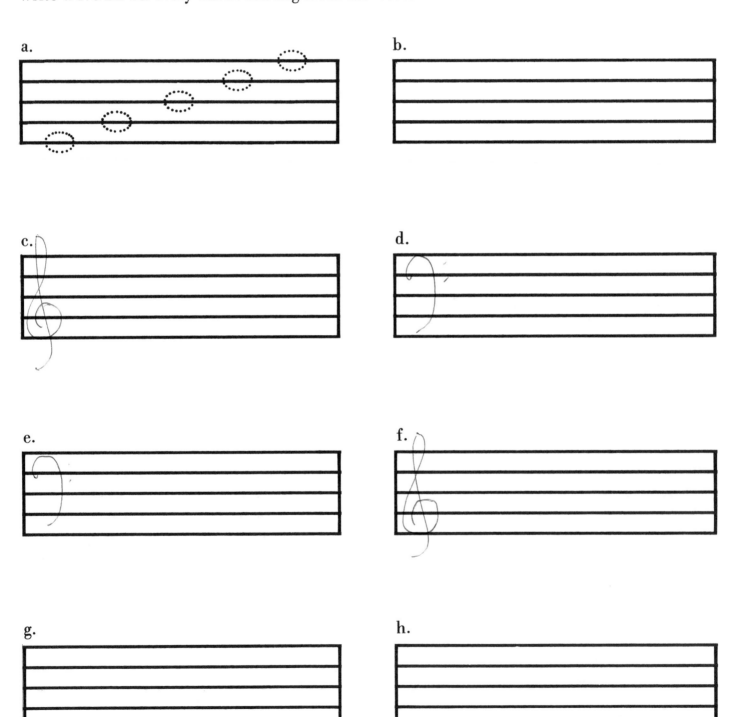

6. **SPACE NOTES** are written between the lines:

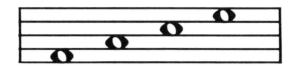

EXERCISES:

Write a **NOTE** in every **SPACE** starting from the **bottom space.**

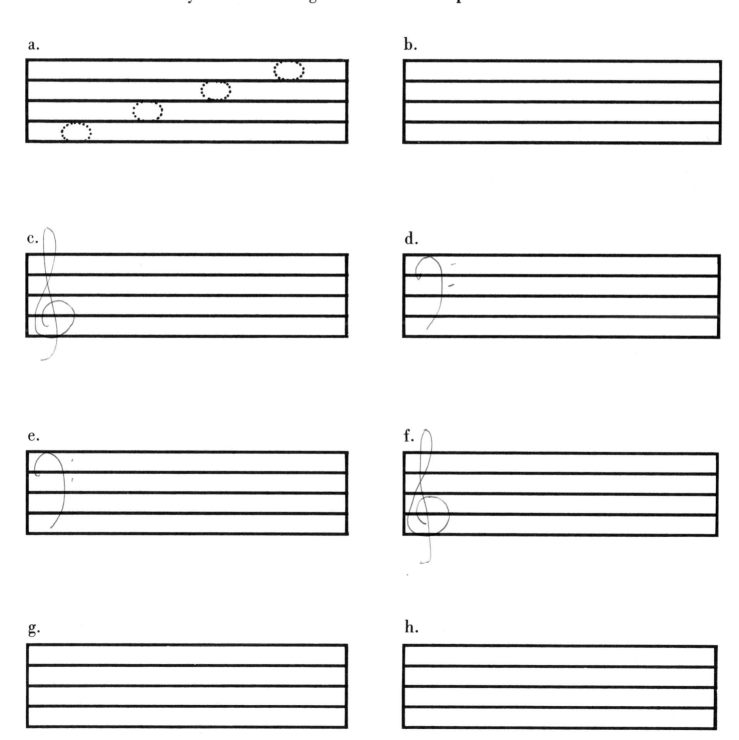

a.

b.

c.

d.

e.

f.

g.

h.

$\frac{166}{100}$

REVIEW No. 2

20 1. **NAME ALL** the **WHITE KEYS** on the keyboard.

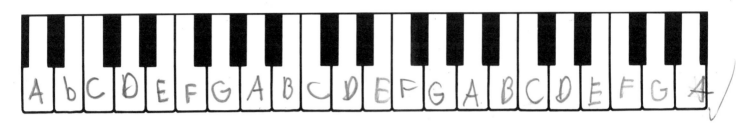

15 2. Write **5 TREBLE CLEFS.**

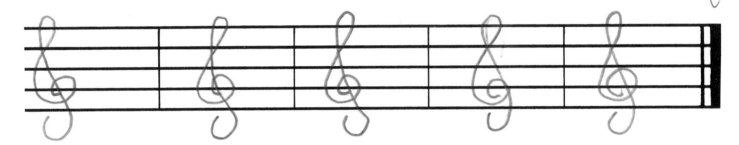

4 3. **NAME** the keys marked with an **"X"**. They spell a word.

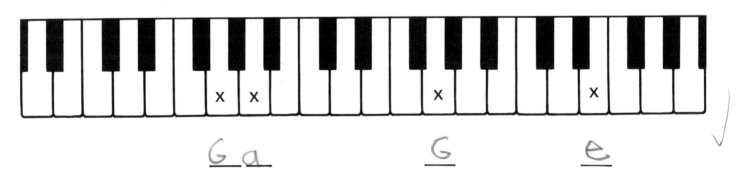

15 4. Write **5 BASS CLEFS.**

3 5. **WRITE** the following **WORD** on the keyboard.

FAD: 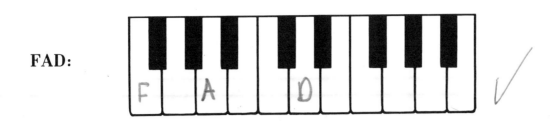 ✓

7 6. What are the **LETTERNAMES** of the **MUSICAL ALPHABET?** ✓

A   B   C   D   E   F   G

18 7. Write the **NUMBERS:**

a. 1 to 5 on the **LINES**   b. 1 to 4 in the **SPACES** ✓

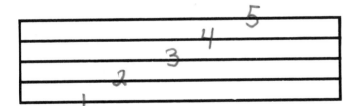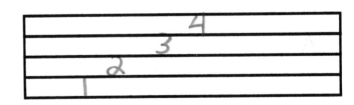

18 8. Write a **NOTE:**

a. on each **LINE.**   b. in each **SPACE.**   *Excellent!*

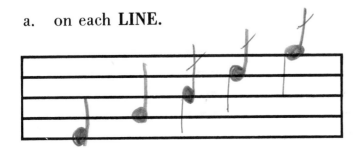

LESSON No. 4
Notes In The Treble Clef

The notes below belong to the treble clef.

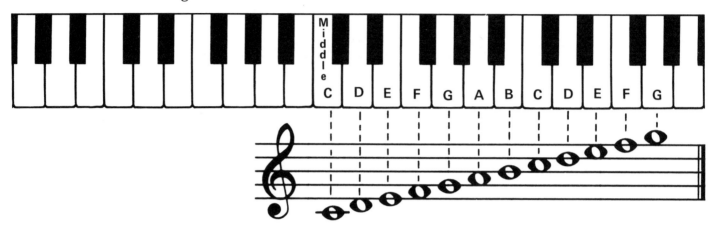

The notes "Middle C" and D are found **BELOW** the

staff in the treble clef.

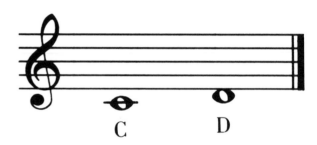

C   D

EXERCISES:

1. Trace the **TREBLE CLEF** and the **MIDDLE C's.**

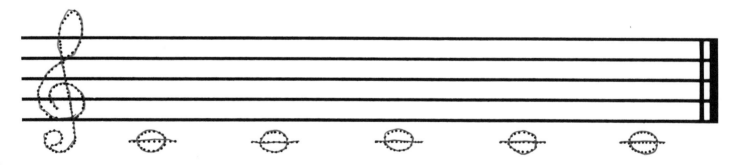

2. Write **5 MIDDLE C's** and **NAME** each note.
   Add a **TREBLE CLEF** to the beginning of the staff.

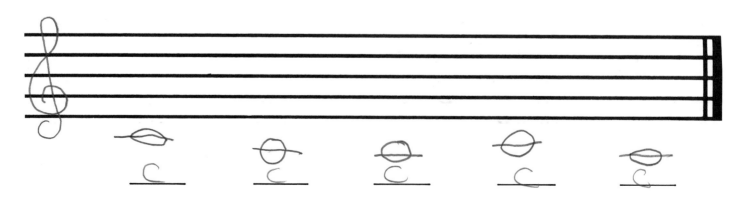

3. Trace the **TREBLE CLEF** and the **D**'s.

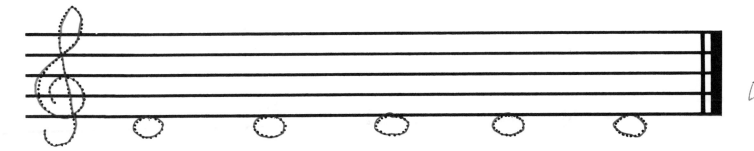

4. Write **5 D's** and **NAME** each one.
   Add a **TREBLE CLEF** to the beginning of the staff.

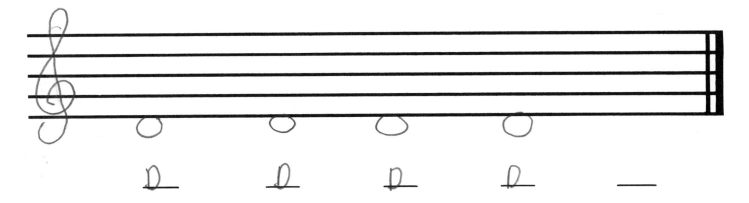

5. **NAME** these notes. Always use **CAPITAL LETTERS**.

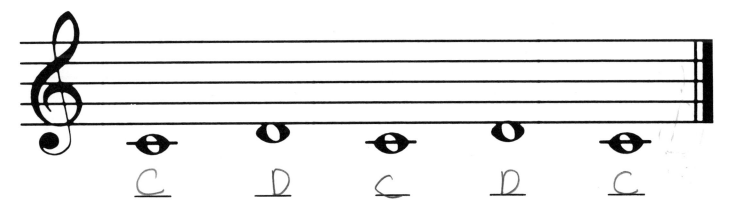

6. Write **NOTES** for the letters below.
   Add a **TREBLE CLEF** to the beginning of the staff.

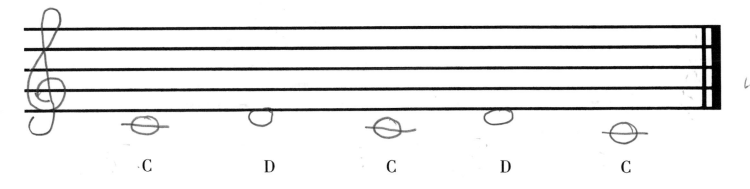

After the notes C and D come the notes E, F, and G.

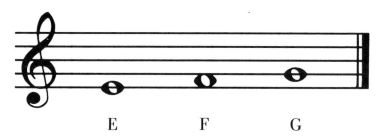

E F G

EXERCISES:

1. Write a **TREBLE CLEF** at the beginning of each staff, then: *Play also*

a. **WRITE** and **NAME 5 E's.** *find 2 E's*

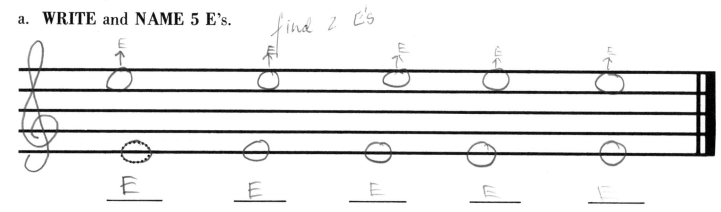

E E E E E

b. **WRITE** and **NAME 5 F's.** *find 2 F's*

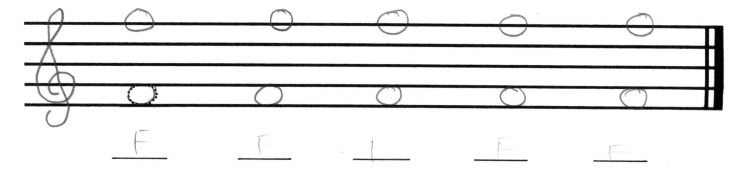

F F F F F

c. **WRITE** and **NAME 5 G's.** *find 2 G's*

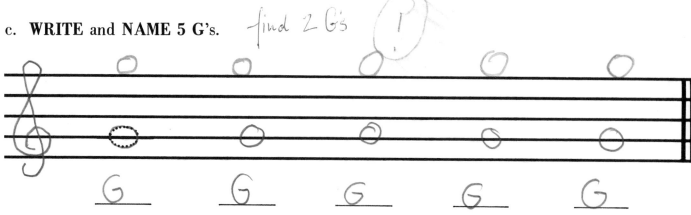

G G G G G

2. Write **NOTES** in the treble clef for the keys marked with an "X" on the keyboard.
   NAME these notes.

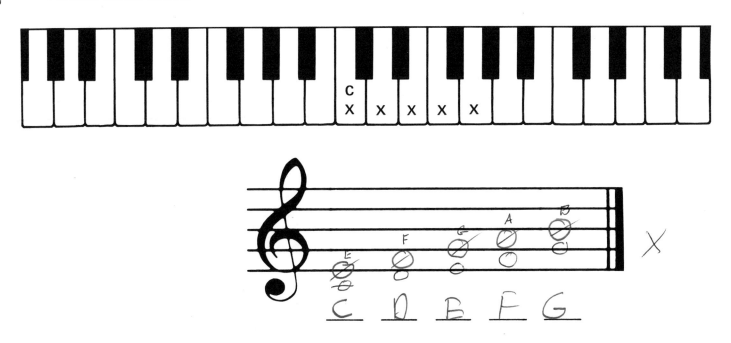

C   D   E   F   G

3. **NAME** these notes.

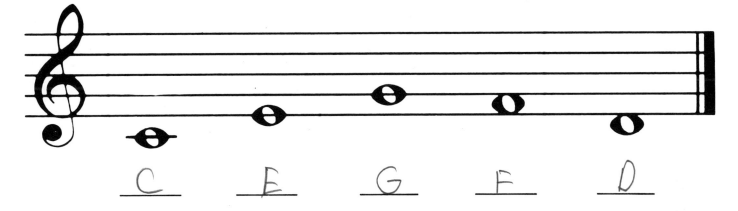

C   E   G   F   D

4. Write **NOTES** for the letters below. Add a **TREBLE CLEF** to the beginning
   of the staff.

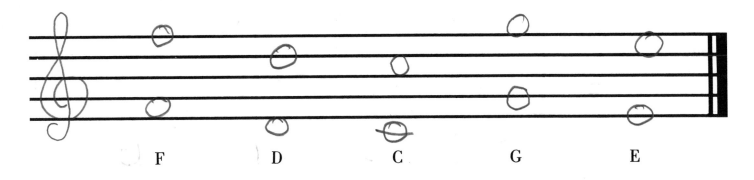

F   D   C   G   E

5. **NAME** these notes and draw corresponding **LINES** to the **KEYBOARD.**

a.

C D E F G

b.

E C G

c.

C E D

6. **WRITE NOTES** for the keys marked with an "X".
   NAME these notes. Add a **TREBLE CLEF** to the beginning of each **STAFF**.

a.

D   G   Clef?

b.

C   F

c.

C   E   G

These are the **LINE NOTES** in the **TREBLE CLEF.**

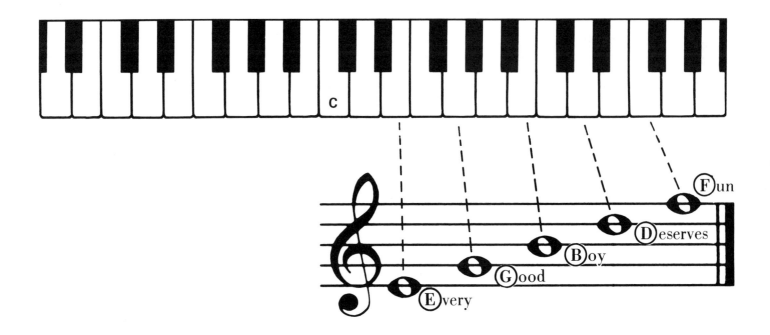

EXERCISES:

1. **NAME** these notes. Add a **TREBLE CLEF** to the beginning of each staff.

a.

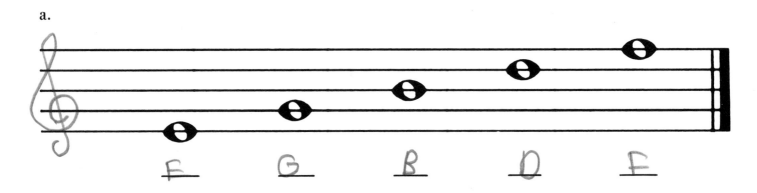

E   G   B   D   F

b.

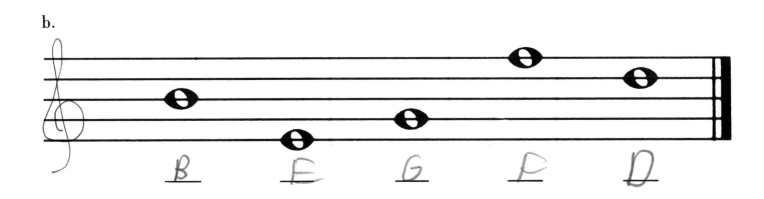

B   E   G   F   D

c. Clef 2.
χ

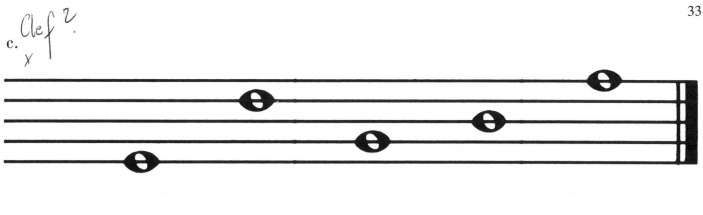

d.
χ

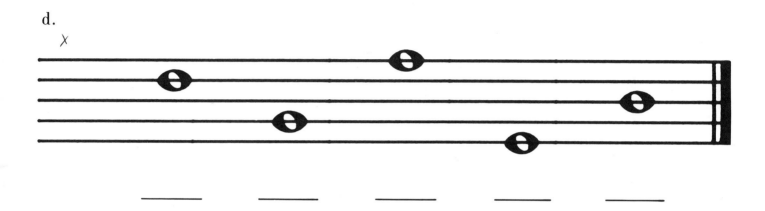

e.
χ

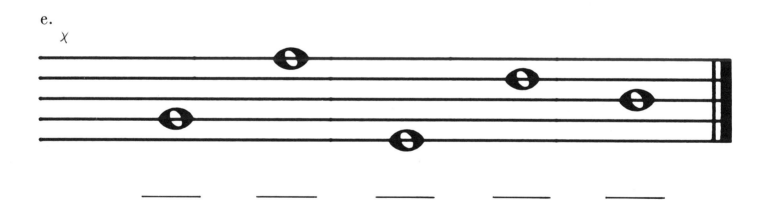

f.
χ

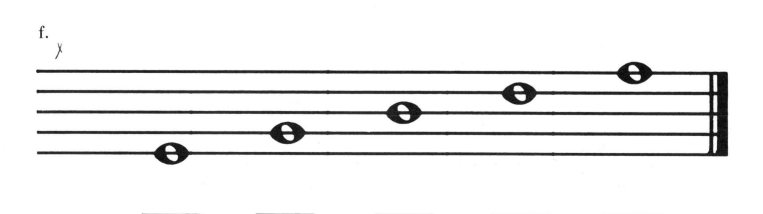

2. Write **LINE NOTES** in the **TREBLE CLEF** for the letters below.

a.

E   G   B   D   F

b.

F   D   B   G   E

c.

D   B   E   F   G

d.

G   F   D   E   B

3. Write **LINE NOTES** in the **TREBLE CLEF** for the keys marked with an "X".
   NAME these notes.

a.

b.

c.

36

4. **NAME** these line notes and draw corresponding **LINES** to the **KEYBOARD**.

a.
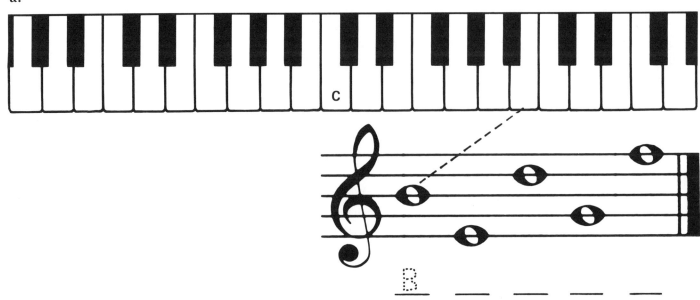

B _ _ _ _ _

b.
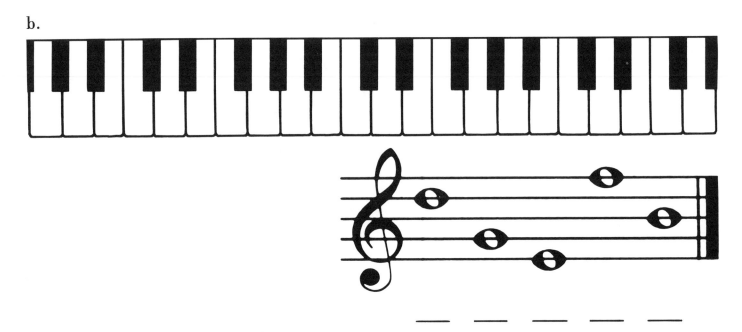

_ _ _ _ _ _

c.
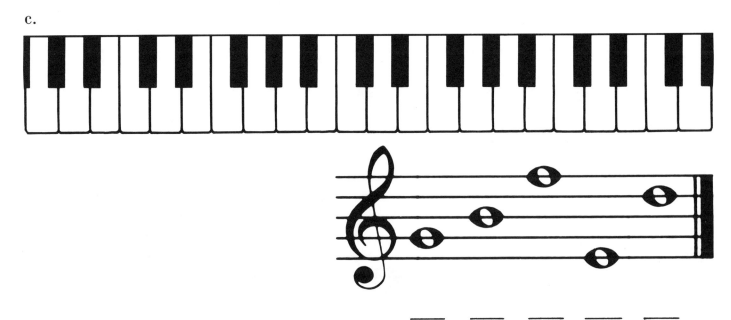

_ _ _ _ _

5. **NAME** the line notes. They spell words.

a.

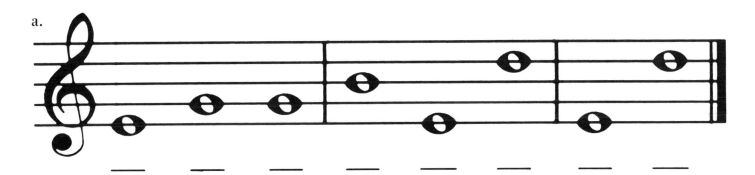

b.

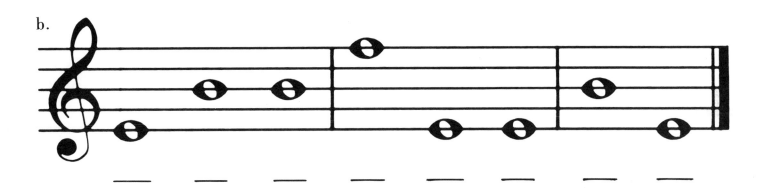

c.

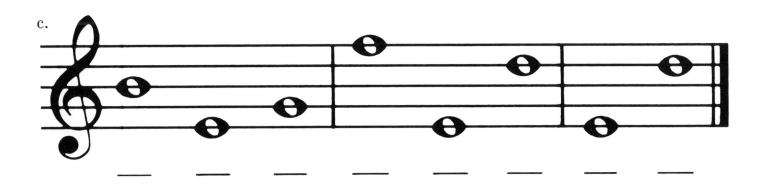

d.

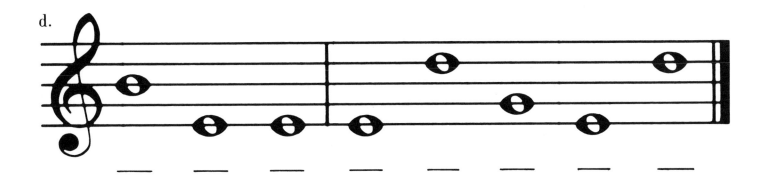

38

6. Write **LINE NOTES** in the **TREBLE CLEF** for the letters below.

a.

B   E   E   F   E   D   G   E

b.

E   G   G   F   E   E   D

c.

D   E   E   D   B   E   E

d.

B   E   G   G   E   D   E   D

REVIEW No. 3

10 1. Write **5 TREBLE CLEFS.**

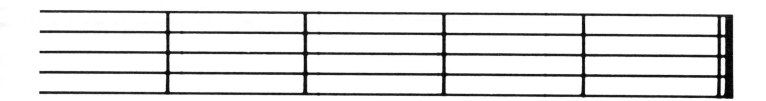

10 2. Write **5 BASS CLEFS.**

7 3. What are the **LETTERNAMES** of the **MUSICAL ALPHABET?**

___ ___ ___ ___ ___ ___ ___

3 4. Write the following **WORD** on the **KEYBOARD.**

A D D: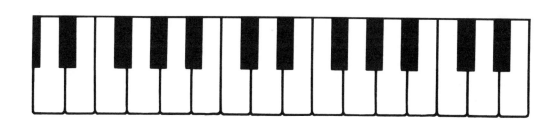

9 5. Write a **NOTE** on each **LINE.**   **NUMBER** the **SPACES**: 1, 2, 3, 4.

20 6. **NAME ALL** the **WHITE KEYS** on the keyboard.

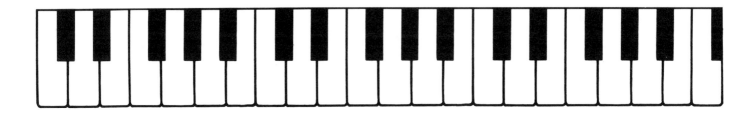

12 7. **NAME** these line notes.

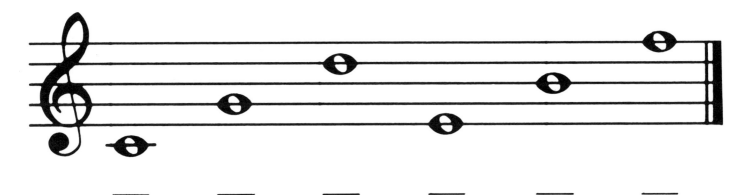

___ ___ ___ ___ ___ ___

4 8. **NAME** the keys marked with an **"X".** They spell a word.

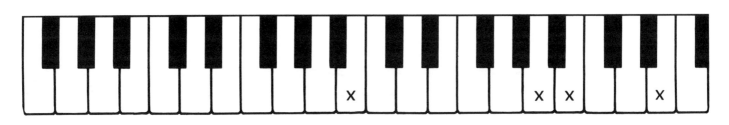

___   ___ ___   ___

8 9. Write **LINE NOTES** in the **TREBLE CLEF** for the letters below.

E   G   B   D   F

10 10. **NAME** these line notes and draw corresponding **LINES** to the **KEYBOARD.**

C

— — — — —

7 11. Write **LINE NOTES** in the **TREBLE CLEF** for the keys marked with an **"X".**
    NAME these notes.

C   X   X

— —   — —

These are the **SPACE NOTES** in the **TREBLE CLEF**.

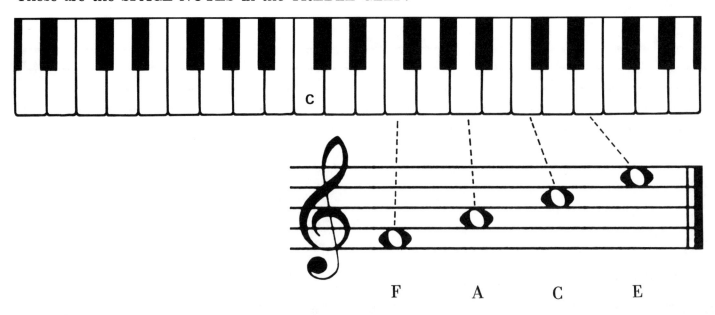

F   A   C   E

EXERCISES:

1. **NAME** these notes. Add a **TREBLE CLEF** to the beginning of each staff.

a.

b.

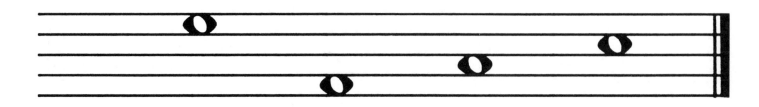

c.

d.

e.

f.

2. Write **SPACE NOTES** in the **TREBLE CLEF** for the letters below.

a.

F   A   C   E

b.

E   C   A   F

c.

A   E   F   C

d.

C   F   E   A

3. **NAME** these space notes and draw corresponding **LINES** to the **KEYBOARD**.

a.

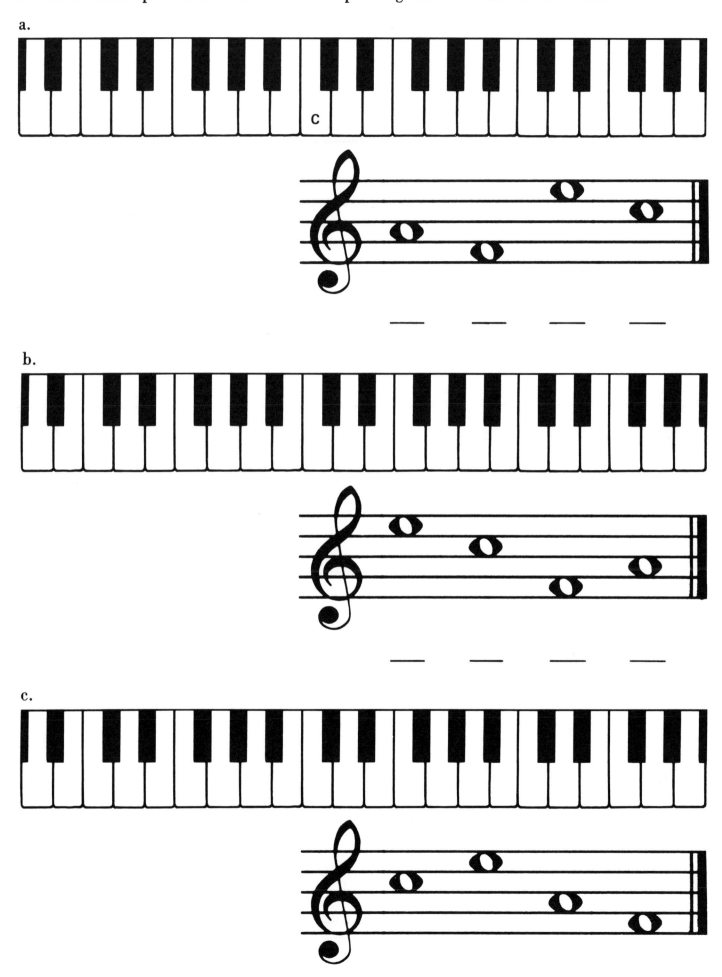

4. Write **SPACE NOTES** in the **TREBLE CLEF** for the keys marked with an **"X"**.
   NAME these notes.

a.

b.

c.

5. **NAME** these notes and draw corresponding **LINES** to the **KEYBOARD**.

a.

b.

c.

6. Write **NOTES** in the **TREBLE CLEF** for the keys marked with an "X".
   NAME these notes.

a.

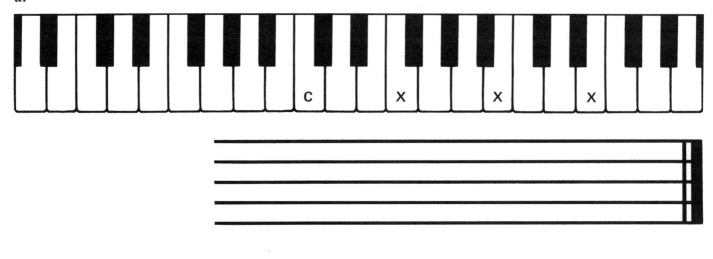

b.

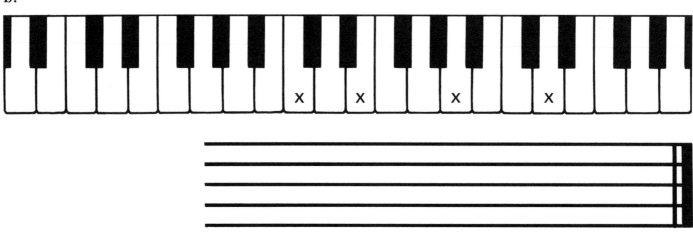

c.

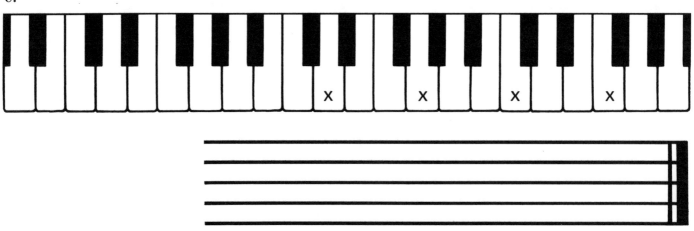

7. **NAME** these notes. They spell words.

a.
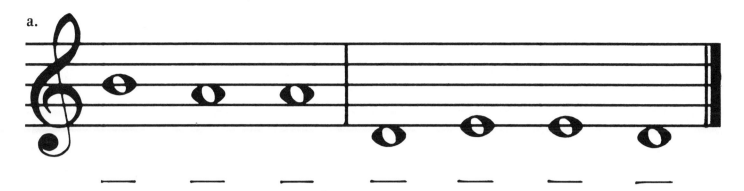

____ ____ ____ ____ ____ ____ ____

b.

____ ____ ____ ____ ____ ____ ____

8. Write **NOTES** in the **TREBLE CLEF** for the letters below.

a.
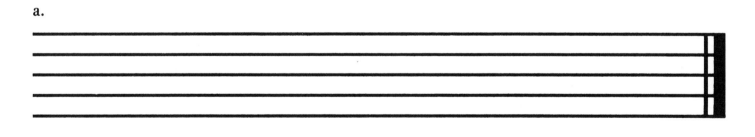

B   A   G   G   A   G   E

b.

C   A   B   B   A   G   E

REVIEW No. 4

7 1. **NAME** these notes. They spell words.

a.
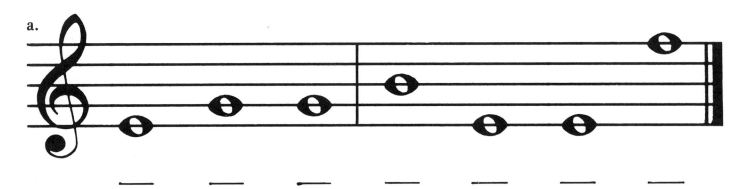

___ ___ ___ ___ ___ ___ ___

b.
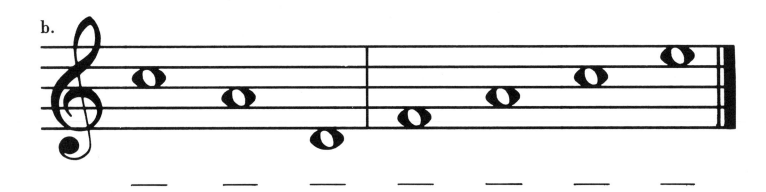

___ ___ ___ ___ ___ ___ ___

5 2. Write 5 **BASS CLEFS.**

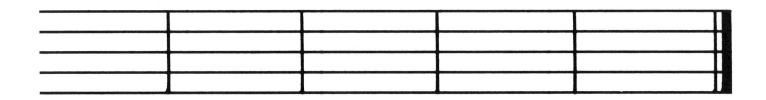

6 3. Write **LINE NOTES** in the **TREBLE CLEF** for the letters below.

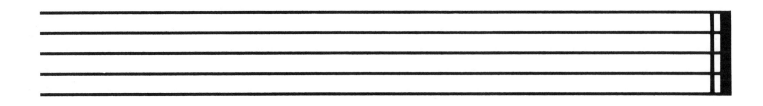

F   D   B   G   E

3 4. Write **SPACE NOTES** in the **TREBLE CLEF** for the keys marked with an **"X"**.
   NAME these notes.

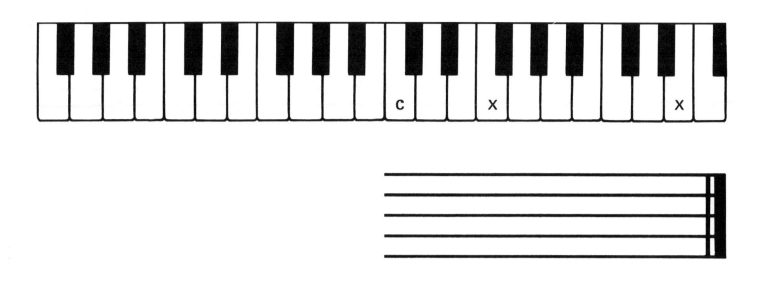

6 5. **NAME** the keys marked with an **"X"**. They spell a word.

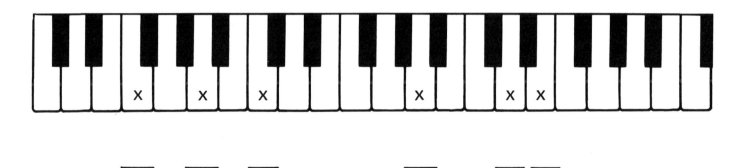

5 6. Write **SPACE NOTES** in the **TREBLE CLEF** for the letters below.

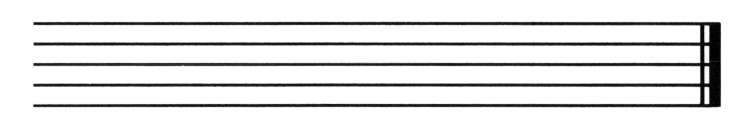

E   A   C   F

7 **7.** Write **NOTES** in the **TREBLE CLEF** for the letters below.

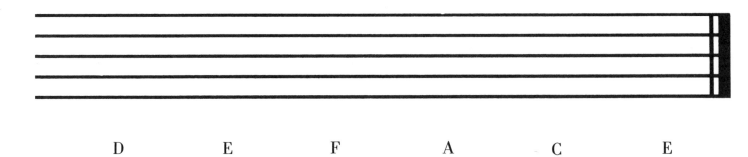

D   E   F   A   C   E

5 **8. NAME** these notes.

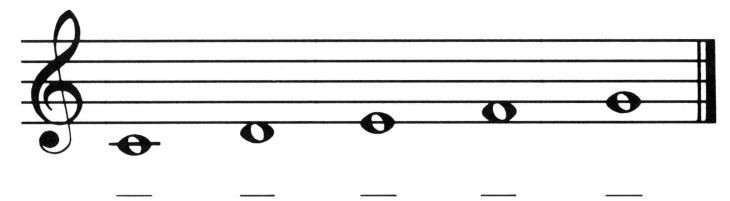

___   ___   ___   ___   ___

6 **9. NAME** these notes and draw corresponding **LINES** to the keys on the **KEYBOARD.**

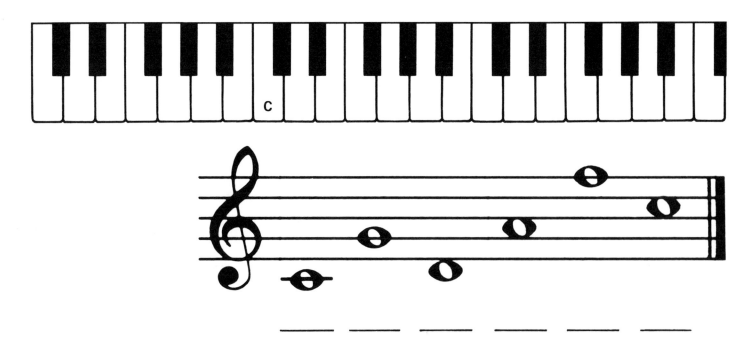

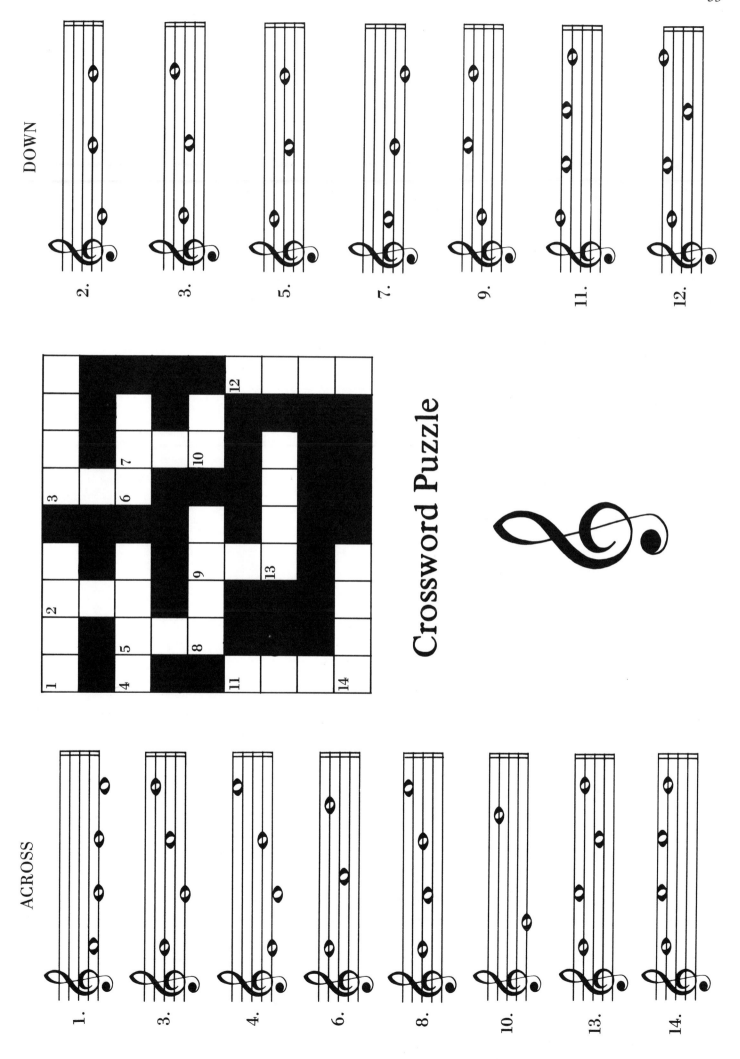

Crossword Puzzle

LESSON No. 5

Notes In The Bass Clef

The notes below belong to the bass clef.

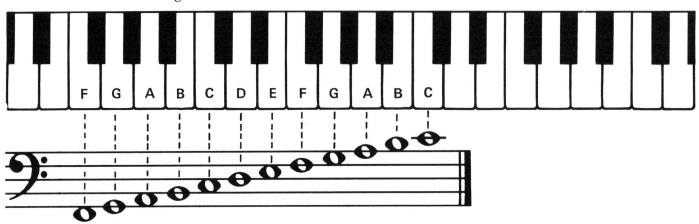

The notes B and "Middle C" are found **ABOVE** the staff in the bass clef.

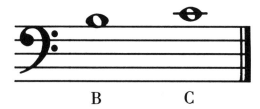

EXERCISES:

1. Trace the **BASS CLEF** and each **B.**

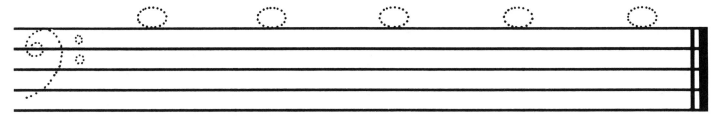

2. Write **5 B's** and **NAME** each note. Add a **BASS CLEF** to the beginning of the staff.

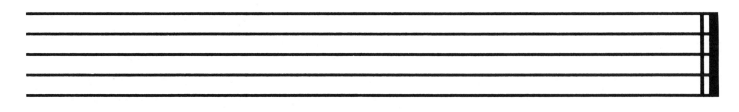

3. Trace the **BASS CLEF** and the **MIDDLE C's.**

4. Write **5 MIDDLE C's** and **NAME** each one. Add a **BASS CLEF** to the beginning of the staff.

5. **NAME** these notes.

6. Write **NOTES** for the letters below. Add a **BASS CLEF** to the beginning of the staff.

B   C   B   C   C

Before the notes B and C come the notes F, G, and A.

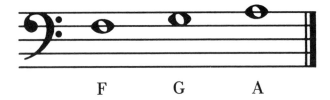

          F   G   A

EXERCISES:

1. Write a **BASS CLEF** at the beginning of each staff, then:

a. **WRITE** and **NAME** 5 F's.

b. **WRITE** and **NAME** 5 G's.

c. **WRITE** and **NAME** 5 A's.

2. Write **NOTES** in the bass clef for the keys marked with an "X" on the keyboard. **NAME** these notes.

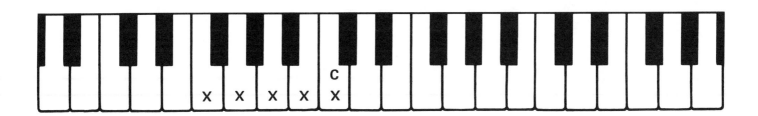

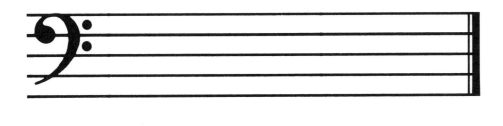

— — — — —

3. **NAME** these notes.

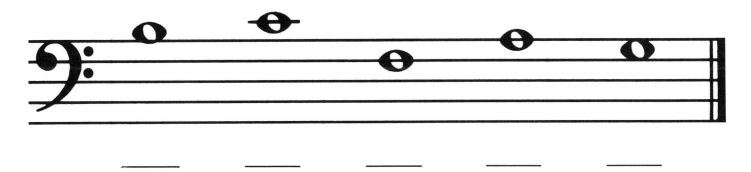

— — — — —

4. Write **NOTES** for the letters below. Add a **BASS CLEF** to the beginning of the staff.

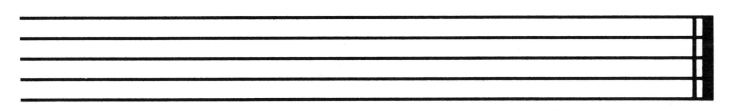

F   G   A   B   C

58

5. **NAME** these notes and draw corresponding **LINES** to the **KEYBOARD**.

a.

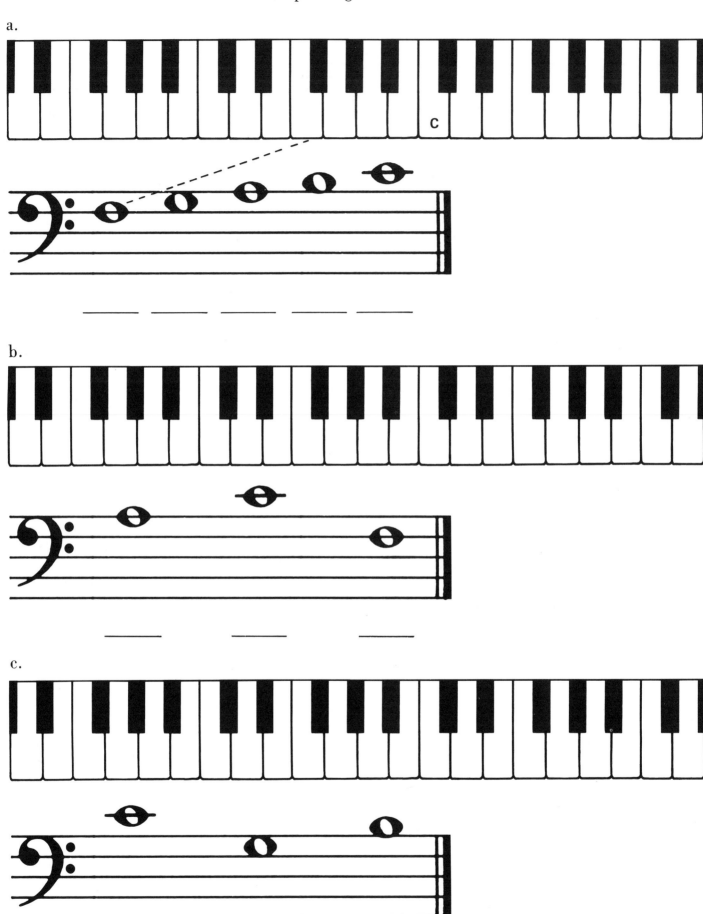

6. Write **NOTES** for the keys marked with an **"X"**. **NAME** these notes.
   Add a **BASS CLEF** to the beginning of the **STAFF**.

a.

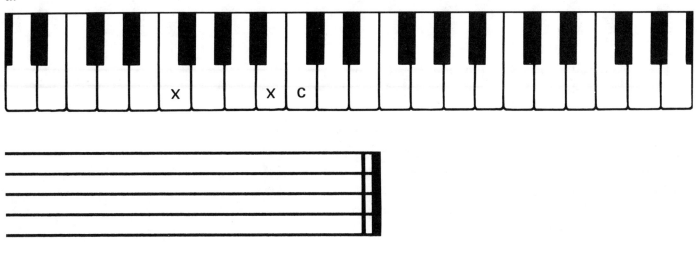

b.

c.

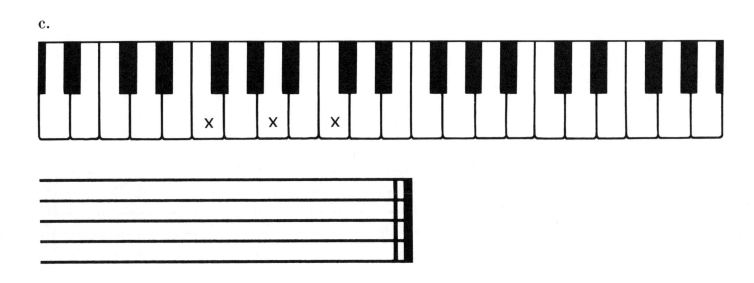

These are the **LINE NOTES** in the **BASS CLEF.**

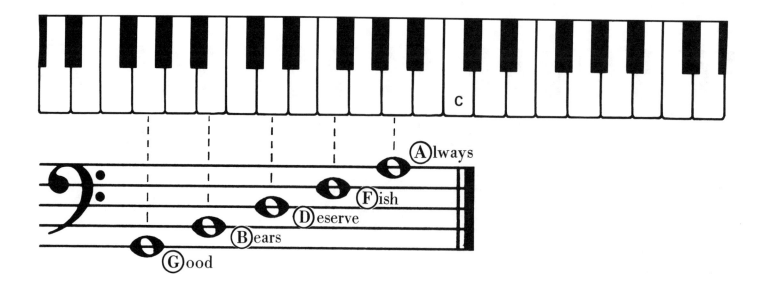

EXERCISES:

1. **NAME** these notes. Add a **BASS CLEF** to the beginning of each staff.

a.

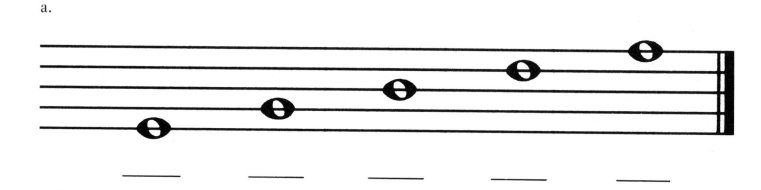

b.

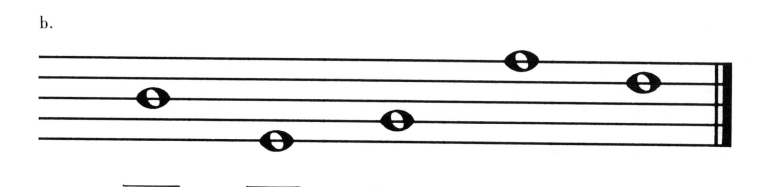

c.

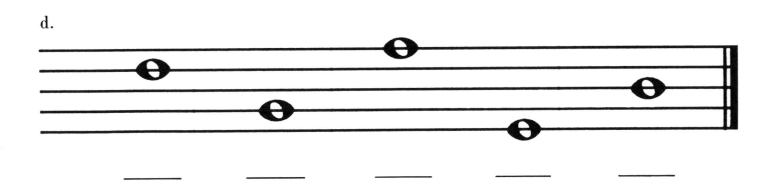

d.

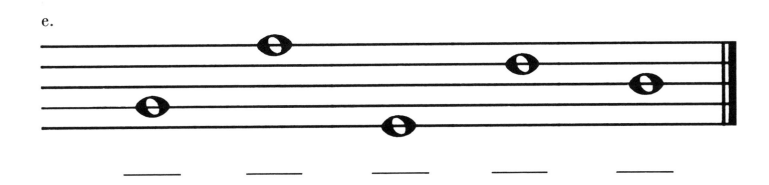

e.

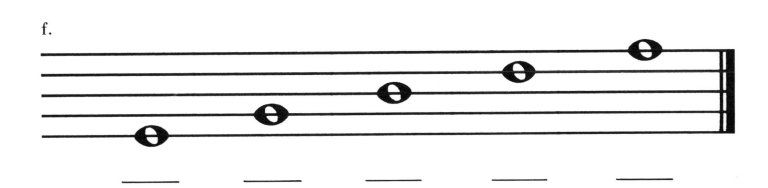

f.

2. Write **LINE NOTES** in the **BASS CLEF** for the letters below.

a.

G   B   D   F   A

b.

A   F   D   B   G

c.

F   G   A   D   B

d.

B   A   F   G   D

63

3. Write **LINE NOTES** in the **BASS CLEF** for the keys marked with an **"X"**.
   NAME each note.

a.

b.

c.

4. **NAME** these line notes and draw corresponding **LINES** to the **KEYBOARD.**

a.

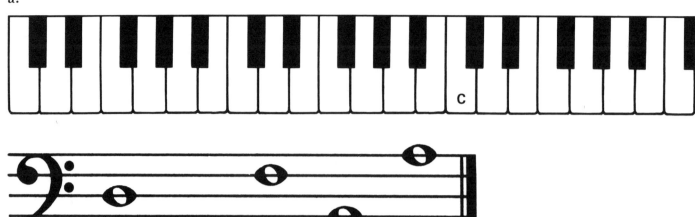

_____ _____ _____ _____ _____

b.

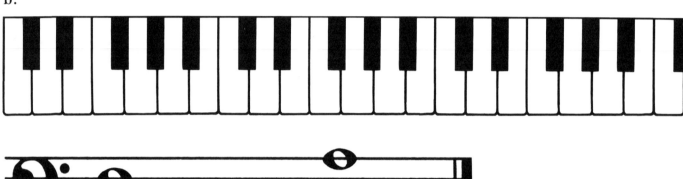

_____ _____ _____ _____ _____

c.

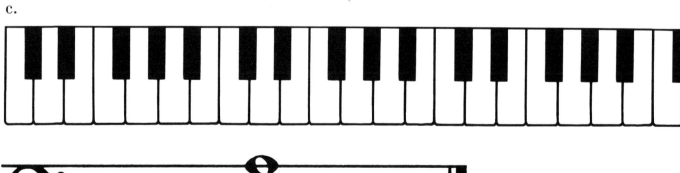

_____ _____ _____ _____ _____

5. **NAME** the line notes. They spell words.

a.

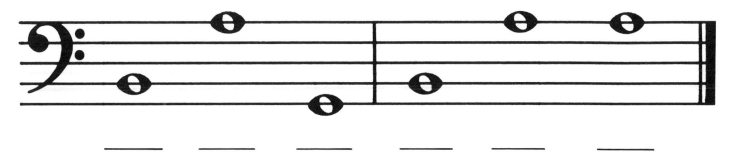

____ ____ ____   ____ ____

b.

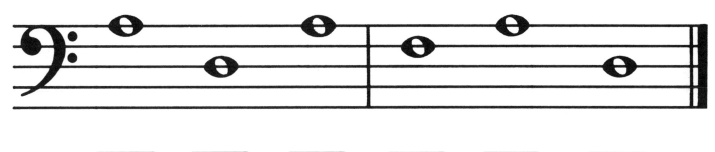

____ ____ ____   ____ ____

c.

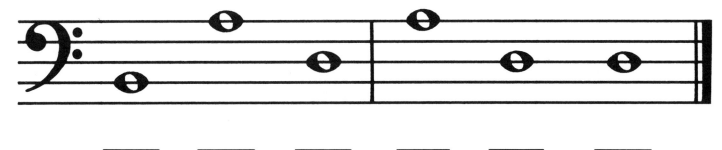

____ ____   ____ ____

d.

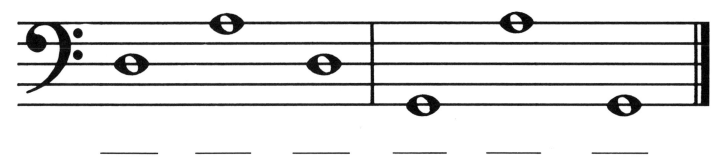

____ ____ ____   ____ ____

6. Write **LINE NOTES** in the **BASS CLEF** for the letters below.

a.

G   A   G   D   A   D

b.

A   D   D   B   A   D

c.

F   A   D   A   D   A

d.

B   A   A   B   A   G

50

REVIEW No. 5

6 1. Write **NOTES** in the **TREBLE CLEF** for the letters below.

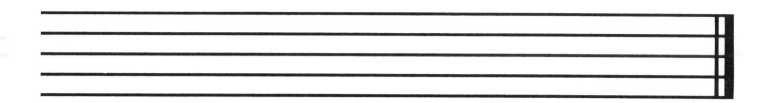

        C   D   E   F   G

3 2. **NAME** these notes and draw corresponding **LINES** to the **KEYBOARD.**

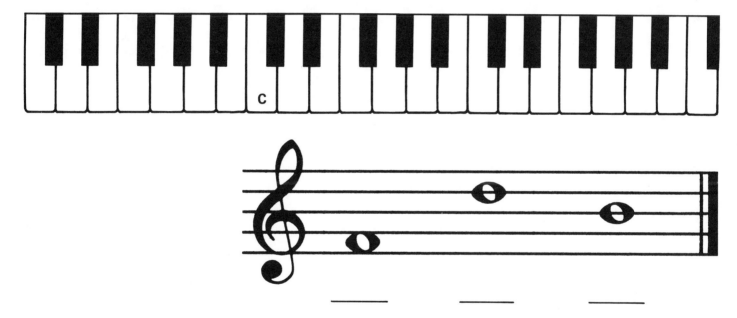

6 3. **NAME** these line notes. They spell words.

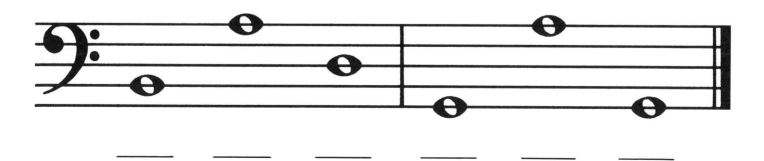

68

5   4. Write **NOTES** in the **TREBLE CLEF** for the letters below.

                    F   A   D   E

5   5. Write **LINE NOTES** in the **BASS CLEF** for the keys marked with an **"X"**.
     NAME each note.

     ____   ____

5   6. **NAME** these notes.

     ____   ____   ____   ____   ____

5   7. Write 4 **MIDDLE C's** in the **BASS CLEF. NAME** each note.

....

c ____   ____   ____   ____

10   8. **NAME** these notes and draw corresponding **LINES** to the **KEYBOARD.**

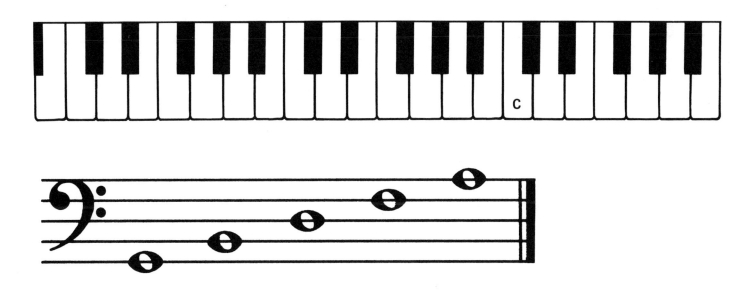

____ ____ ____ ____ ____

5   9. Write 4 **MIDDLE C's** in the **TREBLE CLEF. NAME** each note.

....

____   ____   ____   ____

These are the **SPACE NOTES** in the **BASS CLEF**.

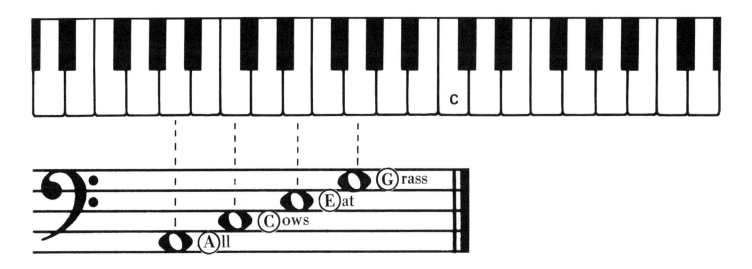

EXERCISES:

1. **NAME** the notes. Add a **BASS CLEF** to the beginning of each staff.

a.

b.

c.

d.

e.

f.

2. Write **SPACE NOTES** in the **BASS CLEF** for the letters below.

a.

A   C   E   G

b.

G   E   C   A

c.

C   A   G   E

d.

E   G   A   C

3. **NAME** these space notes and draw corresponding **LINES** to the **KEYBOARD.**

a.

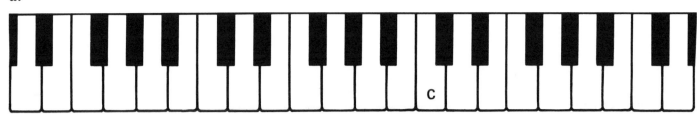

—— —— —— ——

b.

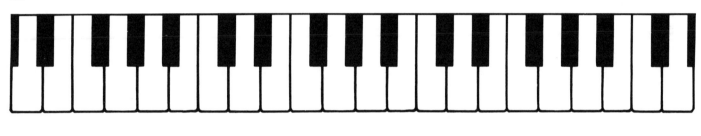

—— —— —— —— ——

c.

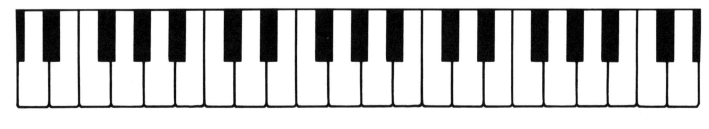

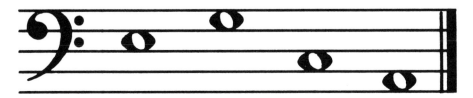

—— —— —— ——

4. Write **SPACE NOTES** in the **BASS CLEF** for the keys marked with an "X".
   NAME these notes.

a.

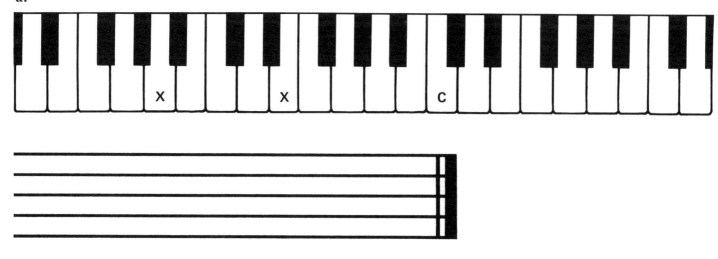

b.

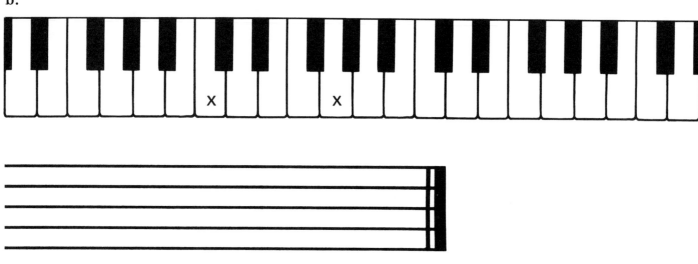

c.

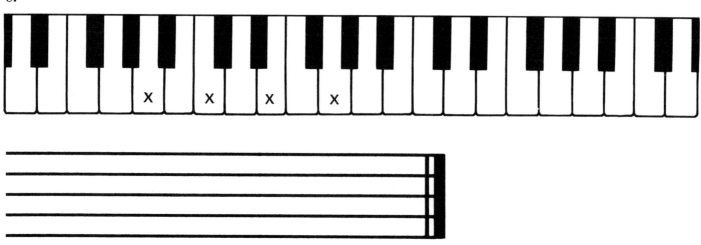

5. **NAME** these notes and draw corresponding **LINES** to the **KEYBOARD**.

a.

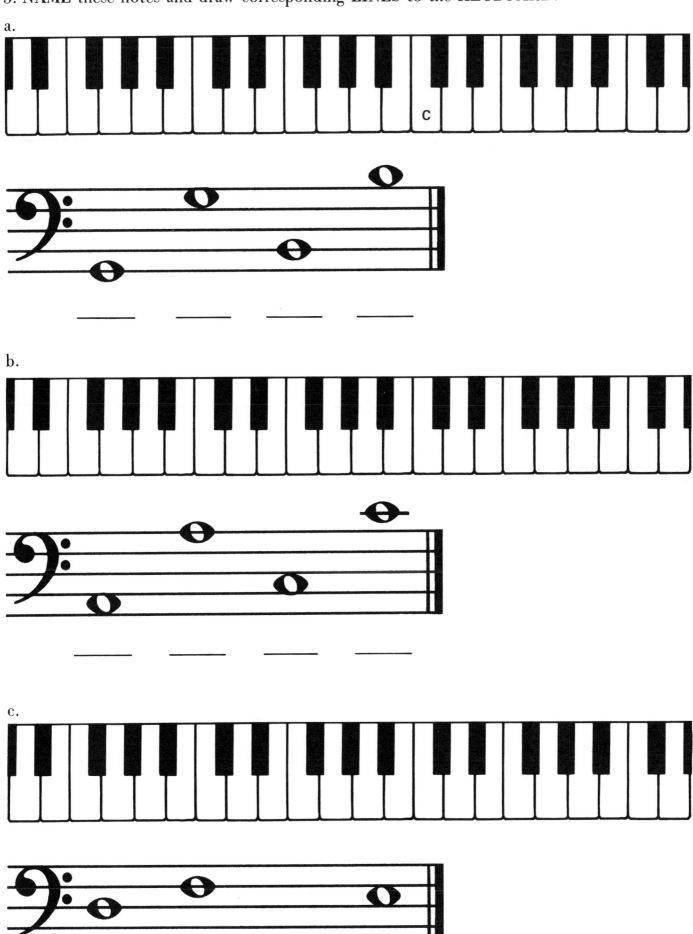

b.

c.

6. Write **NOTES** in the **BASS CLEF** for the keys marked with an **"X"**. **NAME** these notes.

a.

b.

c.

7. **NAME** these notes. They spell **WORDS**.

a.

_ _ _ _ _ _ _ _ _ _ _ _ _ _ _ _

b.
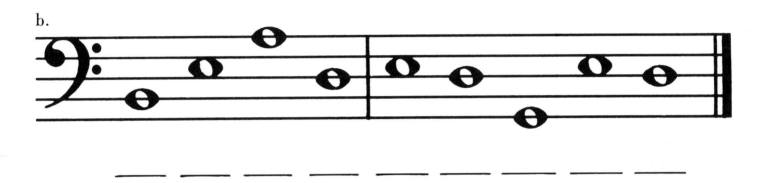

_ _ _ _ _ _ _ _ _ _ _ _ _ _ _ _

8. Write **NOTES** in the **BASS CLEF** for the letters below.

a.
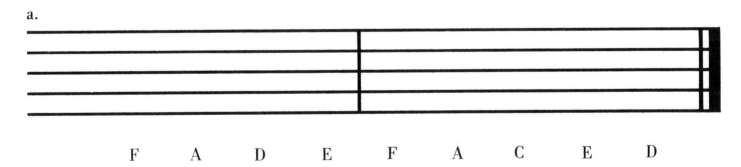

      F   A   D   E   F   A   C   E   D

b.
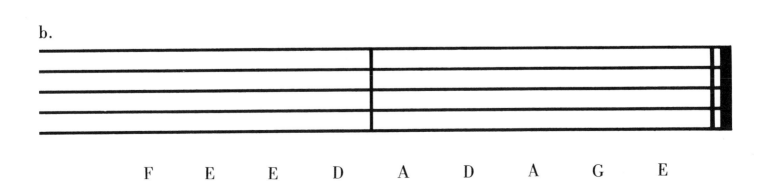

      F   E   E   D   A   D   A   G   E

100

9 1. **NAME** these notes. They spell words.

20 2. Write **NOTES** in the **BASS CLEF** for the letters below.

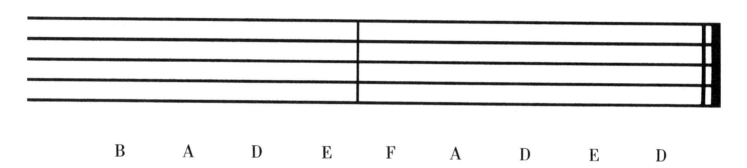

B   A   D   E   F   A   D   E   D

6 3. **NAME** these notes and draw corresponding **LINES** to the **KEYBOARD.**

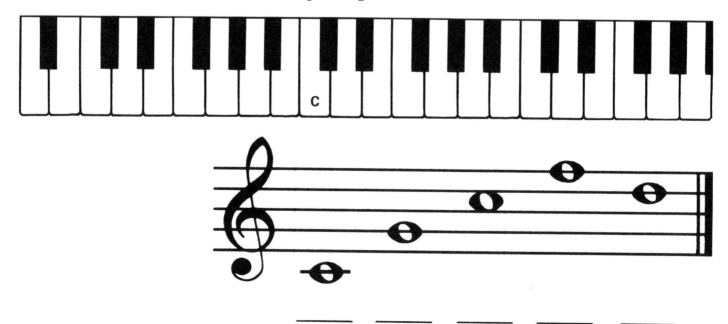

12 **4.** Write **5 MIDDLE C's** in the **TREBLE CLEF**. **NAME** each note.

___   ___   ___   ___   ___

12 **5.** Write **5 MIDDLE C's** in the **BASS CLEF**. **NAME** each note.

___   ___   ___   ___   ___

22 **6.** Write **NOTES** in the **TREBLE CLEF** for the letters below.

E   G   G   B   E   E   F   A   B   E

12 7. Write **NOTES** in the **BASS CLEF** for the keys marked with an **"X"**. **NAME** each note.

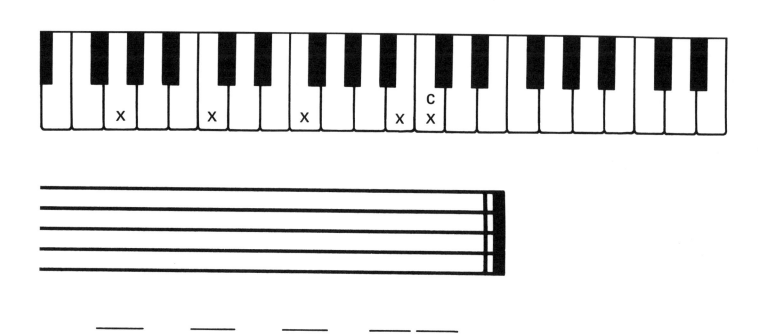

_____   _____   _____   _____   _____

7 8. **NAME** these notes. They spell words:

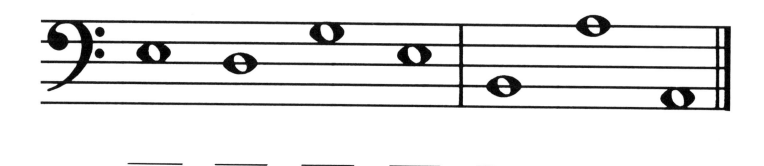

_____ _____ _____ _____   _____ _____ _____

Find The Hidden Sign

Colour each section according to the note it contains:

All **A's** - **YELLOW**   All **D's** - **PINK**   All **F's** - **ORANGE**
All **B's** - **BLUE**   All **E's** - **PURPLE**   All **G's** - **RED**
All **C's** - **GREEN**

NAME the SIGN: _____

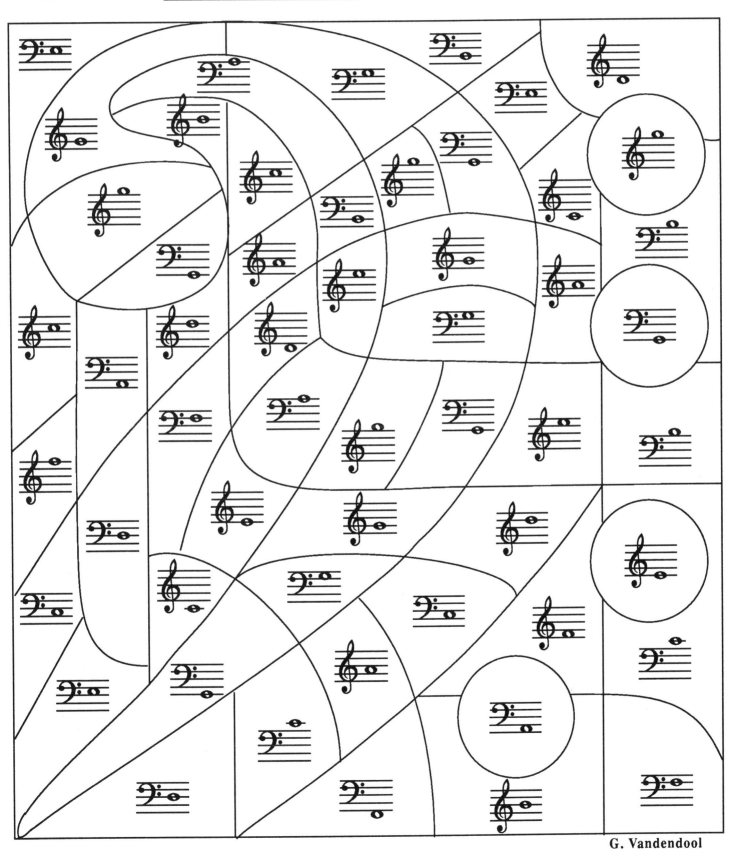

G. Vandendool

LESSON No.6

Time
Note Values

We are black and join hands! We are called **EIGHTH NOTES**.

We get **1 beat** together.

♪♪ = **1**

I am black! I am called a **QUARTER NOTE**. I get **1 beat**.

♩ = **1**

I am white! I am called a **HALF NOTE**. I get **2 beats**.

𝅗𝅥 = **2**

I get a dot! I am called a **DOTTED HALF NOTE**. I get **3 beats**.

𝅗𝅥. = **3**

I am a round ball! I am called a **WHOLE NOTE**. I get **4 beats**.

𝅝 = **4**

EXERCISES:

1. Write 4 pairs of **EIGHTH NOTES**. We get ____ beat together.

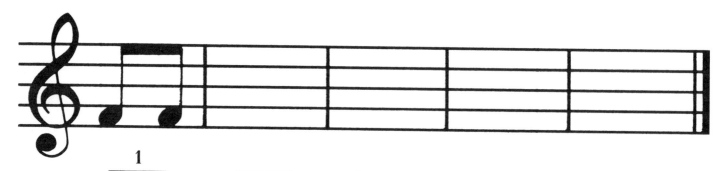

2. Write 4 **QUARTER NOTES**. I get ____ beat.

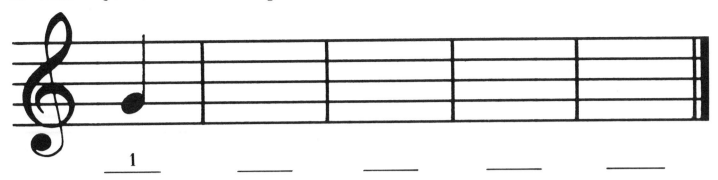

    <u> 1 </u>   <u>   </u>   <u>   </u>   <u>   </u>   <u>   </u>

3. Write 4 **HALF NOTES**. I get ____ beats.

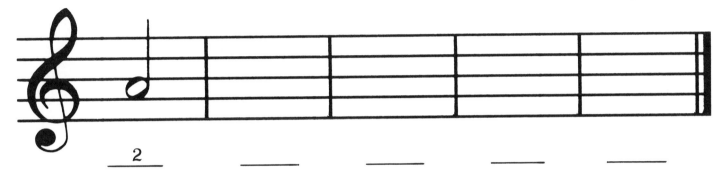

    <u> 2 </u>   <u>   </u>   <u>   </u>   <u>   </u>   <u>   </u>

4. Write 4 **DOTTED HALF NOTES**. I get ____ beats.

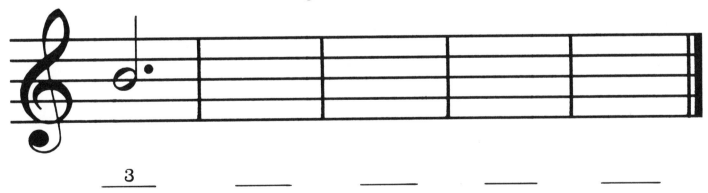

    <u> 3 </u>   <u>   </u>   <u>   </u>   <u>   </u>   <u>   </u>

5. Write 4 **WHOLE NOTES**. I get ____ beats.

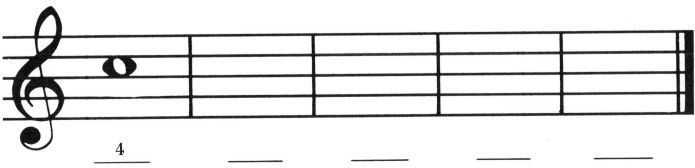

    <u> 4 </u>   <u>   </u>   <u>   </u>   <u>   </u>   <u>   </u>

6. **MATCH** the **NOTES** with the corresponding **NOTE NAMES.**

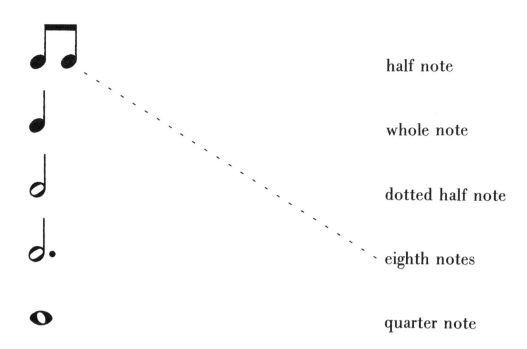

half note

whole note

dotted half note

eighth notes

quarter note

7. **MATCH** the **NUMBER OF BEATS** with the corresponding **NOTES.**

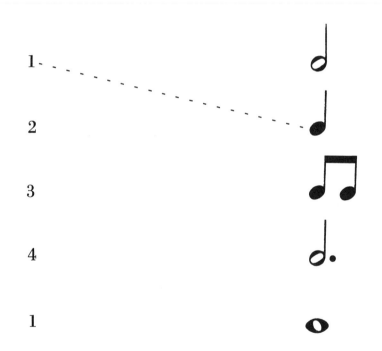

1

2

3

4

1

8. Write the **NUMBER OF BEATS** each note receives.

9. **NAME** each **TYPE OF NOTE.**

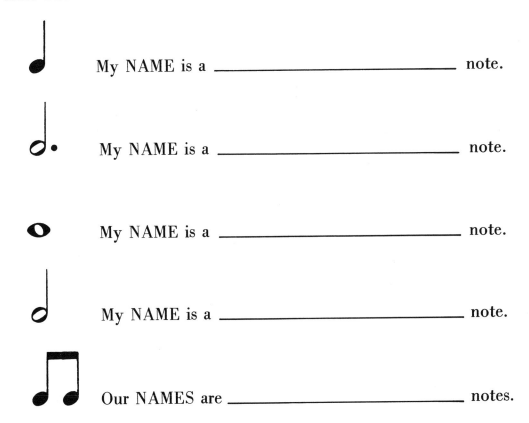

My NAME is a _____ note.

My NAME is a _____ note.

My NAME is a _____ note.

My NAME is a _____ note.

Our NAMES are _____ notes.

10. **MATCH** the **NOTE NAMES** with the correct **NUMBER OF BEATS.**

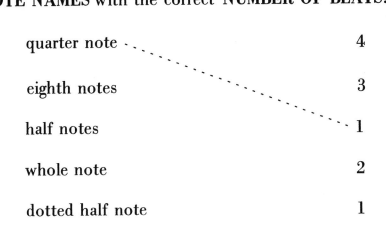

quarter note   4

eighth notes   3

half notes   1

whole note   2

dotted half note   1

11. Write the corresponding **NOTE** for each number below,
using the note **E.**

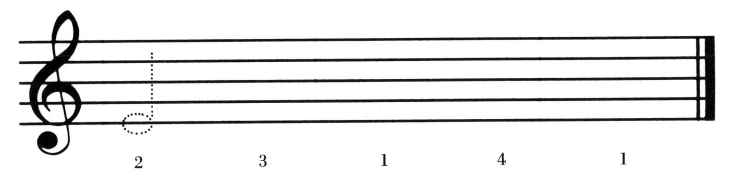

2   3   1   4   1

12. Write the **NUMBER OF BEATS** each note name receives.

        A DOTTED HALF NOTE gets   _____ beats.

        A WHOLE NOTE gets   _____ beats.

        A QUARTER NOTE gets   _____ beat.

        A HALF NOTE gets   _____ beats.

        Two EIGHTH NOTES get   _____ beat.

13. Write the corresponding **NOTE** for each **NOTE NAME.**

        dotted half note =   ♩.

        quarter note   =   _____

        half note   =   _____

        whole note   =   _____

        eighth notes   =   _____

14. Write the **NUMBER OF BEATS** for each note below.

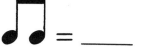

♩ = ____   ♩. = ____   𝅝 = ____   ♫ = ____   ♩ = ____

15. Write the corresponding **NOTE** for each number below.

    2 = ____   1 = ____   3 = ____   4 = ____   1 = ____

16. **ADD** the two **NOTE VALUES**. Write **ONE NOTE** of equal value below each line.

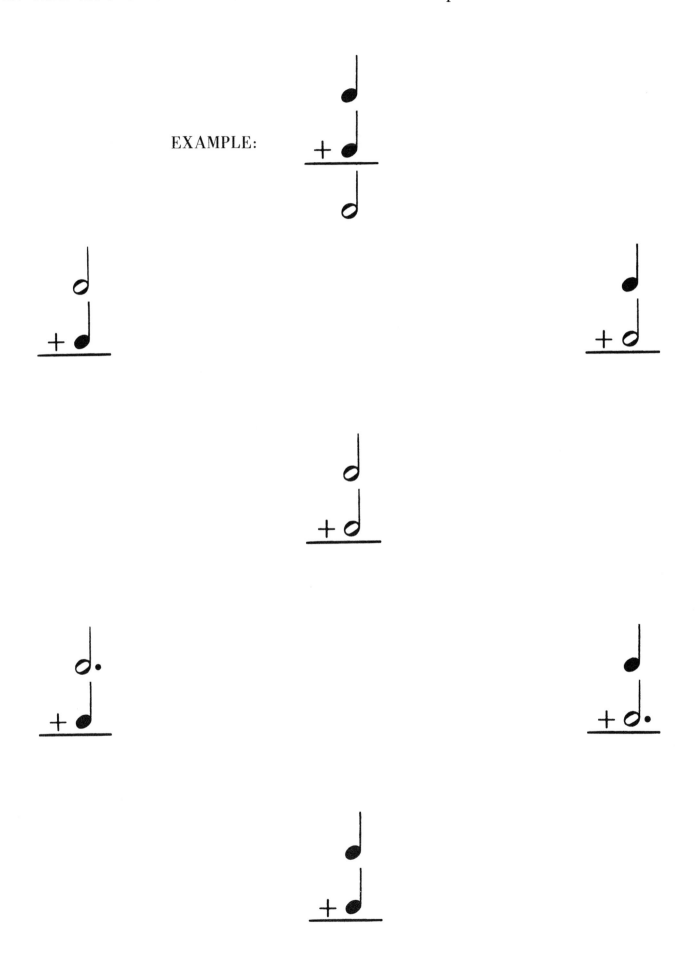

Rest Values

I look like a seven! I am called an **EIGHTH REST.** I get a **1/2 beat.**

I look like a worm! I am called a **QUARTER REST.** I get **1 beat.**

I sit on the 3rd line! I am called a **HALF REST.** I get **2 beats.**

I hang from the 4th line! I am called a **WHOLE REST.** I get **4 beats.**

EXERCISES:

1. Write 4 **EIGHTH RESTS**. I get _____ a beat.

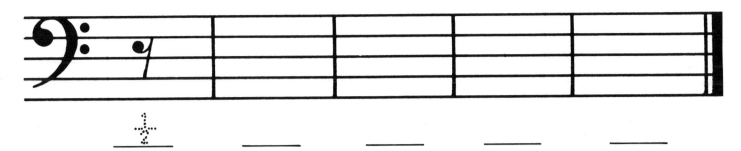

2. Write 4 **QUARTER RESTS**. I get _____ beat.

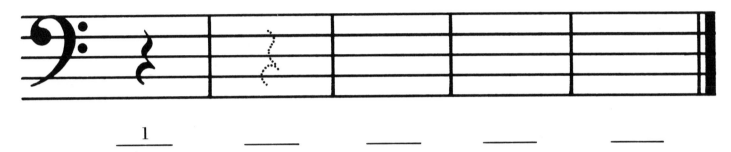

      <u>1</u>

3. Write 4 **HALF RESTS**. I get _____ beats.

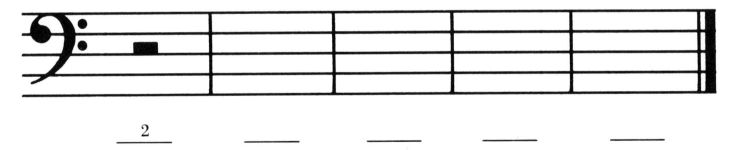

      <u>2</u>

4. Write 4 **WHOLE RESTS**. I get _____ beats.

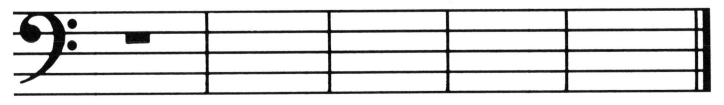

      <u>4</u>

5. MATCH the RESTS with the corresponding REST NAMES.

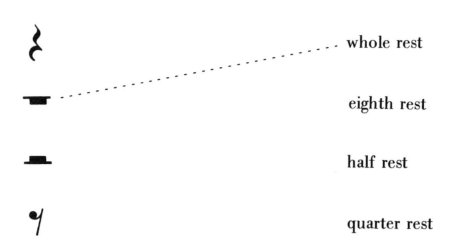

6. MATCH the NUMBER OF BEATS with the corresponding REST.

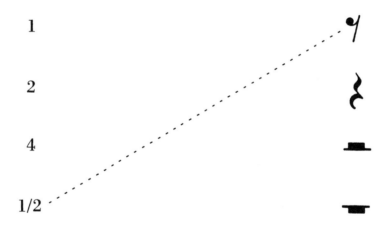

7. Write the **NUMBER OF BEATS** for each rest.

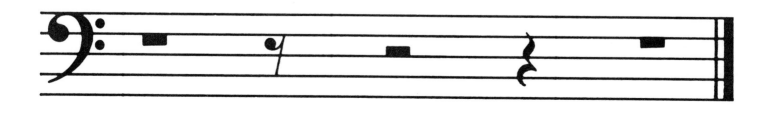

8. **NAME** each type of rest.

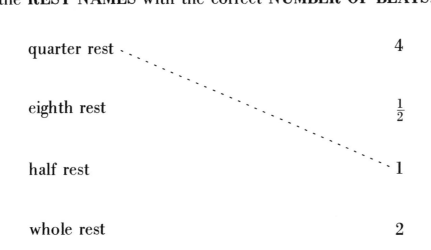

__half__ rest.

_____ rest.

_____ rest.

_____ rest.

9. **MATCH** the **REST NAMES** with the correct **NUMBER OF BEATS.**

quarter rest   4

eighth rest $\frac{1}{2}$

half rest   1

whole rest   2

10. Write the corresponding **REST** for each number below.

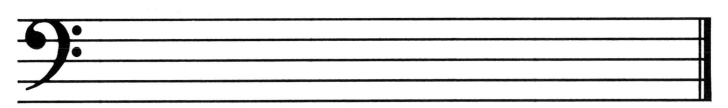

1   1/2   4   2

11. Write the **NUMBER OF BEATS** each rest name receives.

A WHOLE REST gets   _____ beats.

An EIGHTH REST gets   _____ a beat.

A HALF REST gets   _____ beats.

A QUARTER REST gets   _____ beat.

12. Write the corresponding **REST** for each rest name.

quarter rest   =   _____

half rest   =   _____

whole rest   =   _____

eighth rest   =   _____

13. **MATCH** the **NOTE** with the **REST** of equal value.

14. Fill in the missing **RESTS**.

♩ + 𝄽 = 2   𝅗𝅥 + ___ = 4

___ + ♩ = 3   ___ + ♩ = 5

♫ + ___ = 2   𝅗𝅥. + ___ = 4

15. Fill in the missing **NOTES**.

___ + 𝄽 = 4   ▬ + ___ = 5

▬ + ___ = 4   ___ + ▬ = 5

___ + ▬ = 4   𝄽 + ___ = 5

16. Write the **REST** which equals the value of the note.

♩ = ___   ♪ = ___   𝅝 = ___   𝅗𝅥 = ___

LESSON No. 7

Common Terms and Signs

SIGN	WORD	MEANING
p	*piano*	soft
mp	*mezzo piano*	a little louder than *p*
mf	*mezzo forte*	a little softer than *f*
f	*forte*	loud
	staccato	detached
	crescendo	gradually louder
	decrescendo	gradually softer
♭	flat	lowers the note a semitone
♯	sharp	raises the note a semitone
♮	natural	cancels a sharp or a flat
:‖	repeat	play a section over agaim
	tie	connects two notes of the same pitch; adds the time value of the second note.
	phrase	a musical sentence
	slur	connects two notes of a different pitch

REVIEW No. 7

22 1. Write **NOTES** in the **TREBLE CLEF** for the letters below.

      D   E   A   D   E   G   G   C   A   B

15 2. Write the correct **NAME** and **BEAT** for each time value.

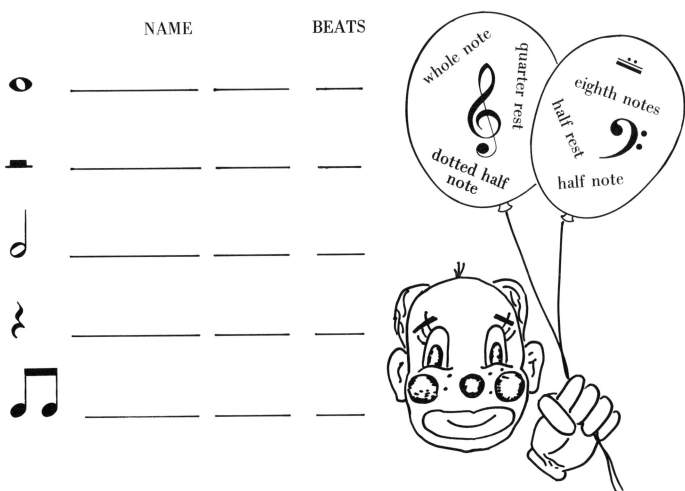

NAME   BEATS

9 3. **NAME** these notes. They spell **WORDS.**

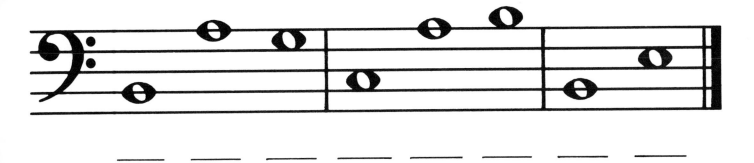

96

10   4. **NAME** these notes and draw corresponding **LINES** to the **KEYBOARD.**

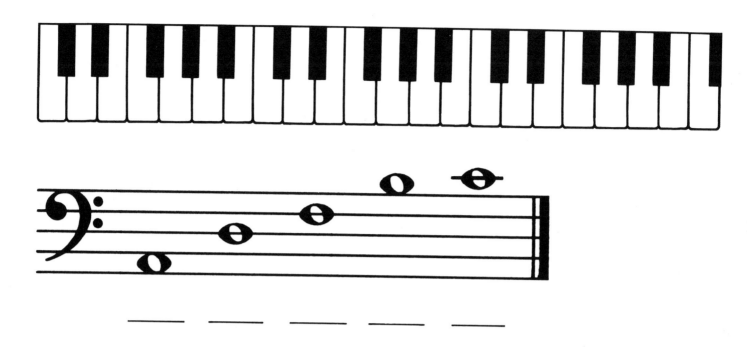

_____   _____   _____   _____   _____

10   5. **MATCH** the **NOTES** with the **RESTS** of equal time value.

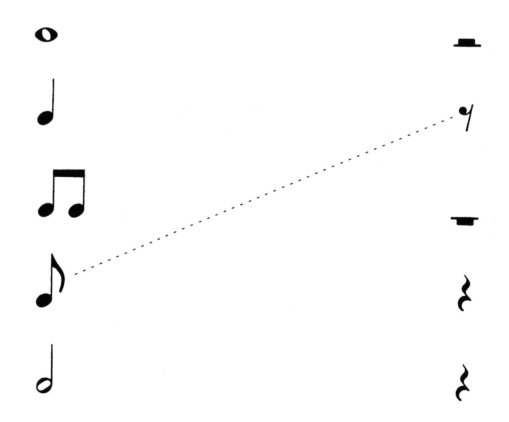

6. Write **NOTES** in the **TREBLE CLEF** for the keys marked with an **"X"**.
NAME each note.

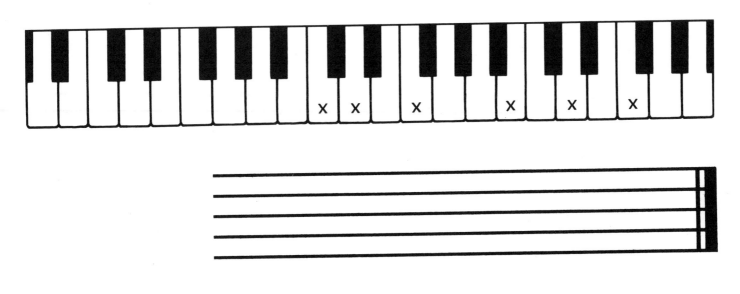

10 7. **MATCH** the **SIGNS** with the **MUSICAL TERMS.**

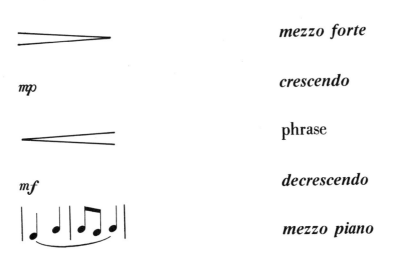

mezzo forte

crescendo

phrase

decrescendo

mezzo piano

10 8. **MATCH** the **SIGNS** with the **MUSICAL MEANINGS.**

p

loud

gradually louder

f

soft

gradually softer

detached

Colour the clown and colour all the
  4 beat time values in **RED**
  3 beat time values in **PURPLE**
  2 beat time values in **YELLOW**
  1 beat time values in **BLUE**
  ½ beat time values in **GREEN**